Natalie King, Sam Holyman and Clai

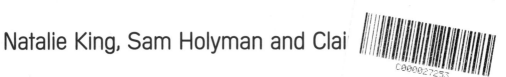

# ESSENTIALS

## OCR GCSE

## Additional Science B

# Contents

Revised

**2** Fundamental Scientific Processes

## Biology

### B3: Living and Growing

**4** B3a Molecules of Life
**6** B3b Proteins and Mutations
**8** B3c Respiration
**9** B3d Cell Division
**11** B3e The Circulatory System
**13** B3f Growth and Development
**15** B3f New Genes for Old
**17** B3g Cloning
**20** B3 Exam Practice Questions

### B4: It's a Green World

**22** B4a Ecology in the Local Environment
**26** B4b Photosynthesis
**28** B4c Leaves and Photosynthesis
**29** B4d Diffusion and Osmosis
**32** B4e Transport in Plants
**34** B4f Plants Need Minerals
**35** B4g Decay
**37** B4h Farming
**40** B4 Exam Practice Questions

## Chemistry

**42** Fundamental Chemical Concepts

### C3: Chemical Economics

**46** C3a Rate of Reaction (1)
**47** C3b Rate of Reaction (2)
**49** C3c Rate of Reaction (3)
**50** C3d Reacting Masses
**52** C3e Percentage Yield and Atom Economy
**53** C3f Energy
**55** C3g Batch or Continuous?
**56** C3h Allotropes of Carbon and Nanochemistry
**58** C3 Exam Practice Questions

# Contents

Revised

**C4: The Periodic Table**

60 C4a Atomic Structure

63 C4b Ionic Bonding

66 C4c The Periodic Table and Covalent Bonding

68 C4d The Group 1 Elements

70 C4e The Group 7 Elements

72 C4f Transition Elements

73 C4g Metal Structure and Properties

74 C4h Purifying and Testing Water

76 C4 Exam Practice Questions

## Physics

**P3: Forces for Transport**

78 P3a Speed

80 P3b Changing Speed

82 P3c Forces and Motion

84 P3d Work and Power

85 P3e Energy on the Move

86 P3f Crumple Zones

88 P3g Falling Safely

90 P3h The Energy of Games and Theme Rides

92 P3 Exam Practice Questions

**P4: Radiation for Life**

94 P4a Sparks

96 P4b Uses of Electrostatics

97 P4c Safe Electricals

100 P4d Ultrasound

102 P4e What is Radioactivity?

105 P4f Uses of Radioisotopes

106 P4g Treatment

107 P4h Fission and Fusion

110 P4 Exam Practice Questions

112 Answers

115 Glossary of Key Words

118 Periodic Table

IBC Index

# Fundamental Scientific Processes

Scientists carry out **experiments** and collect **evidence** in order to explain how and why things happen. Scientific knowledge and understanding can lead to the **development of new technologies** which have a huge impact on **society** and the **environment**.

**Scientific evidence** is often based on data that has been collected through **observations** and **measurements**. To allow scientists to reach conclusions, evidence must be **repeatable**, **reproducible** and **valid**.

## Models

**Models** are used to explain scientific ideas and the universe around us. Models can be used to describe:

- a complex idea like how heat moves through a metal
- a system like the Earth's structure.

Models make a system or idea easier to understand by only including the most important parts. They can be used to explain real world observations or to make predictions. But, because models don't contain all the **variables**, they do sometimes make incorrect predictions.

Models and scientific ideas may change as new observations are made and new **data** are collected. Data and observations may be collected from a series of experiments. For example, the accepted model of the structure of the atom has been modified as new technology and further experiments have produced new evidence.

## Hypotheses

Scientific explanations are called **hypotheses**. Hypotheses are used to explain observations. A hypothesis can be tested by planning experiments and collecting data and evidence. For example, if you pull a metal wire you may observe that it stretches. This can be explained by the scientific idea that the atoms in the metal are in layers and can slide over each other. A hypothesis can be modified as new data is collected, and may even be disproved.

## Data

**Data** can be displayed in **tables**, **pie charts** or **line graphs**. In your exam you may be asked to:

- choose the most appropriate method for displaying data
- identify trends
- use the data mathematically, including using statistical methods, calculating the **mean** and calculating gradients on graphs.

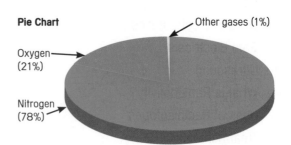

**Pie Chart**

Other gases (1%)
Oxygen (21%)
Nitrogen (78%)

**Line Graph**

Data can be predicted
Data can't be predicted
Dependent Variable (e.g. production)
Independent Variable (e.g. year)

**Table**

| Pressure (Atmospheres) | Yield (%) Temperature (°C) | | | |
|---|---|---|---|---|
| | 250 | 350 | 450 | 550 |
| 200 | 73 | 50 | 28 | 13 |
| 400 | 77 | 65 | 45 | 26 |

Model • Variable • Data • Hypothesis

## Data (Cont.)

Sometimes the same data can lead to different conclusions. For example, data shows that the world's average temperatures have been rising significantly over the last 200 years. Some scientists think this is due to increased combustion of fossil fuels, whilst other scientists think it's a natural change seen before in Earth's history.

## Scientific and Technological Development

Every scientific or technological development could have effects that we do not know about. This can give rise to **issues**. An issue is an important question that is in dispute and needs to be settled. Issues could be:

- **Social** – they impact on the human population of a community, city, country, or the world.
- **Environmental** – they impact on the planet, its natural ecosystems and resources.
- **Economic** – money and related factors like employment and the distribution of resources.
- **Cultural** – what is morally right and wrong; a value judgement must be made.

**Peer review** is a process of self-regulation involving experts in a particular field who **critically examine** the work undertaken. Peer review methods are designed to maintain standards and provide **credibility** for the work that has been carried out. The methods used vary depending on the type of work and also on the overall purpose behind the review process.

## Evaluating Information

**Conclusions** can then be made based on the scientific evidence that has been collected and should try to explain the results and observations.

**Evaluations** look at the whole investigation. It is important to be able to evaluate information relating to social-scientific issues. When evaluating information:

- make a list of **pluses** (pros)
- make a list of **minuses** (cons)
- consider how each point might **impact on society**.

You also need to consider whether the source of information is reliable and credible and consider opinions, bias and weight of evidence.

**Opinions** are personal viewpoints. Opinions backed up by valid and reliable evidence carry far more weight than those based on non-scientific ideas. Opinions of experts can also carry more weight than opinions of non-experts. Information is **biased** if it favours one particular viewpoint without providing a balanced account. Biased information might include incomplete evidence or try to influence how you interpret the evidence.

# B3 Molecules of Life

## Cells

Fundamental processes of life take place inside cells. All cells contain the following:

- **Cytoplasm**, where chemical reactions take place.
- A **cell membrane**, which allows movement into and out of the cell.
- A **nucleus**, which contains the genetic information and controls what the cell does.
- **Mitochondria** – **respiration** takes place inside mitochondria, supplying energy for the cell. Cells that have a high energy requirement, e.g. sperm cells, muscle cells and liver cells, have large numbers of mitochondria.

(HT) Some structures are too small to see with a light microscope, e.g. ribosomes. Ribosomes are in the cytoplasm and are the site of protein synthesis.

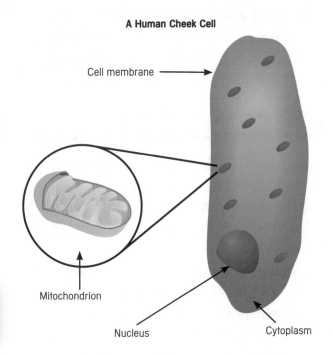

**A Human Cheek Cell**

Cell membrane

Mitochondrion

Nucleus

Cytoplasm

## Genetic Information

Inside the nucleus of every cell are **chromosomes** which carry genetic information in the form of **genes**. A **gene** is a region of chromosome that carries information about, and **controls**, a particular inherited **characteristic**.

The order (or sequence) of the bases provides the **genetic code** (instructions) that controls cell activity. Each gene has a different sequence of bases. The DNA molecules in a cell form a complete set of **instructions** for how the organism should be constructed and how its individual cells should work.

The **nucleus** of each cell contains a complete set of **genetic instructions**. The instructions are carried by **genes** on **chromosomes**. Chromosomes are long coiled molecules of DNA, divided up into regions called genes. Genes are made from a chemical called **DNA** (deoxyribonucleic acid).

Most body cells have the same number of chromosomes, in **matching pairs** – human cells have **23 pairs**.

**Gametes** (sex cells) contain individual chromosomes and therefore have exactly half the number of normal cells.

**DNA Molecule Carries the Genetic Code**

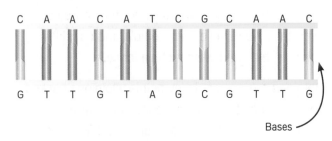

**Uncoiled DNA Molecule – The Bases Code for the Protein**

| C | A | A | C | A | T | C | G | C | A | A | C |
|---|---|---|---|---|---|---|---|---|---|---|---|
| G | T | T | G | T | A | G | C | G | T | T | G |

Bases

## DNA

**DNA** controls the production of proteins. Proteins are needed for growth and repair.

The information in genes is in the form of coded instructions called the **genetic code**. The genetic code controls cell activity and consequently some characteristics of the organism.

A DNA molecule is made of two strands coiled around each other in a **double helix** (spiral). The genetic instructions are in the form of a chemical code made up of four **bases**. These **bases** bond together in specific pairs, forming cross-links.

Each gene contains a different sequence of bases. Genes are like recipes for proteins; each gene codes for a particular protein.

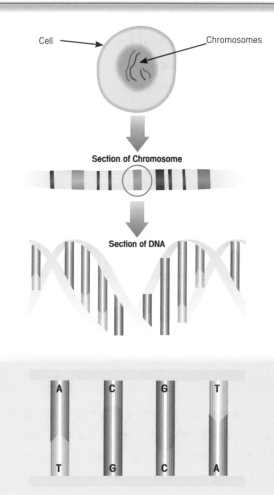

(HT) The four bases in DNA are **A**, **C**, **G** and **T**.

On opposite strands of the DNA molecule:

- A always bonds with T
- C always bonds with G

This is complementary 'base pairing'.

### Structure of DNA

The structure of DNA was first worked out by two scientists, **Watson and Crick**. They used data from other scientists to build a model of DNA. X-ray data showed there were two chains wound in a helix and other data indicated that the bases occurred in pairs.

(HT) New discoveries like Watson and Crick's are not accepted or rewarded immediately. It's important that other scientists can repeat their work and get similar results.

## Proteins

**Proteins** are made in the cytoplasm, but genes can't leave the nucleus so a copy of the gene is needed, which can leave the nucleus.

(HT) The **sequence of bases** in a gene represents the order in which the cell should assemble amino acids to make the protein. A group of **three bases** represents **one amino acid** in a protein chain. Each protein has a different shape and function.

The code needed to produce a protein is carried from the DNA in the nucleus to the ribosomes in the cytoplasm by a molecule called **mRNA**. DNA controls cell function by controlling the production of proteins, some of which are enzymes.

# B3 Proteins and Mutations

## Proteins

**Proteins** are made of long chains of **amino acids**. Their functions include:

- structural, e.g. collagen
- hormones, e.g. insulin
- carrier molecules, e.g. haemoglobin
- enzymes.

Different cells and different organisms will produce different proteins.

(HT) Each protein has its own number and sequence of amino acids. This results in different shapes of molecule.

It is estimated that there are over 19 000 different proteins in the human body, each with a particular function.

## Enzymes

**Enzymes** are **proteins** which act as biological **catalysts**. They speed up chemical reactions, including those that take place in living cells, e.g. respiration, photosynthesis and protein synthesis.

Enzymes are highly specific. Each one will only speed up a **particular** reaction. Enzyme activity, and therefore the rate of a reaction, can be affected by changes in **temperature** or **pH level**.

## The Lock and Key Mechanism

Each **enzyme** has an **active site** that only a specific reactant can fit into (like a key in a lock). High temperatures and extremes of pH stop the lock and key mechanism working.

(HT) When enzyme molecules are exposed to high temperatures or extreme pH, the following occurs:

1. The bonds holding the shape of the protein break.
2. The shape of the enzyme's active site is **denatured** (changed irreversibly).
3. The 'lock and key' mechanism no longer works.

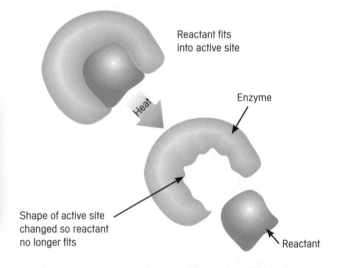

Reactant fits into active site

Heat

Enzyme

Shape of active site changed so reactant no longer fits

Reactant

## Enzyme Activity and pH

The graph alongside shows how changes in pH affect enzyme activity. There is an optimum pH at which the enzyme works best. As the pH increases or decreases, the enzyme becomes less and less effective.

(HT) The active site is damaged irreversibly; the enzyme shape is permanently changed (**denatured**). The lock and key no longer fit.

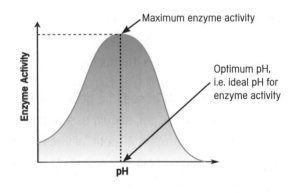

Maximum enzyme activity

Optimum pH, i.e. ideal pH for enzyme activity

Enzyme Activity

pH

## Enzyme Activity and Temperature

The graph below shows the effect of temperature on enzyme activity:

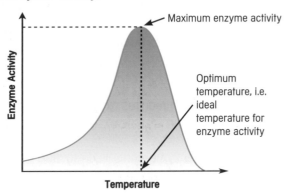

Temperatures above the optimum damage the enzyme molecules irreversibly, decreasing or stopping enzyme activity.

(HT) This is because the shape is changed (denatured) so the lock and key no longer fit. A rise in temperature increases the frequency of collisions between reactants and enzymes, and will increase the enzyme activity until the optimum temperature is reached. At lower temperatures there are lower collision rates slowing down the rate of the reaction.

Different enzymes have different optimum temperatures. The ones in the human body work best at about 37°C.

## (HT) Measuring the Rate of a Reaction

The rate of an enzyme-controlled reaction can be expressed as a $Q_{10}$ value by comparing the rate at a certain temperature and dividing it by the rate of a temperature 10°C lower:

$$Q_{10} = \frac{\text{Rate at temperature, } t}{\text{Rate at temperature, } t - 10°C}$$

## Mutations

Gene **mutations** are changes to **genes**. These changes can be spontaneous, but the rate can be increased by environmental factors such as radiation or chemicals. **Most** mutations are **harmful**, although **occasionally** a **beneficial mutation** occurs. Mutations may lead to production of different proteins.

(HT) Mutations change the base sequence of **DNA**. This alters the shape and function of the protein or prevents the production of the protein that the gene normally codes for.

Only some of the full set of genes are used in any one cell; some genes are switched off. The genes that are switched on determine the function of the cell.

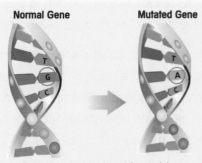

The G base is substituted for an A base

## Quick Test

1 Where does respiration take place in a cell?
2 (HT) How do the four bases in DNA pair up?

# B3 Respiration

## Aerobic Respiration

Energy needed for all life processes in plants and animals is provided by respiration. Life processes require energy from respiration. These include muscle contraction, protein synthesis and control of body temperature in mammals.

**Aerobic respiration** is the release of energy from glucose in the presence of oxygen. It takes place inside all cells.

During exercise, muscles demand more energy so respiration must go faster to release more energy. Breathing and pulse rate increase to deliver oxygen and glucose to muscles more quickly and remove carbon dioxide from muscles quickly.

To investigate how heart rate responds to exercise, take your resting heart rate. Immediately after exercise, take your heart rate, then take it every minute until it returns to resting. This is the **recovery rate** and is a measure of fitness.

You can compare respiration rates by using the respiratory quotient formula:

$$RQ = \frac{carbon\ dioxide\ produced}{oxygen\ used}$$

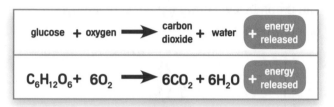

$$glucose + oxygen \longrightarrow carbon\ dioxide + water + energy\ released$$

$$C_6H_{12}O_6 + 6O_2 \longrightarrow 6CO_2 + 6H_2O + energy\ released$$

(HT) Aerobic respiration requires oxygen and so the rate of oxygen consumption is an estimate of metabolic rate.

Respiration is an enzyme-controlled reaction and so its rate is influenced by pH or temperature.

Respiration results in the production of **ATP**, which is used as the energy source for many processes in cells.

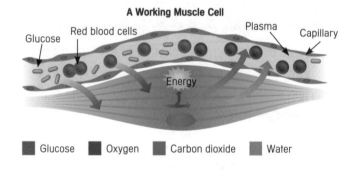

**A Working Muscle Cell**

Glucose · Oxygen · Carbon dioxide · Water

## Anaerobic Respiration

**Anaerobic respiration** occurs when your muscles are working so hard that your lungs and circulatory system can't deliver enough oxygen to break down all the available glucose through aerobic respiration.

Anaerobic respiration takes place in the absence of oxygen. It quickly releases a small amount of energy through the **incomplete** breakdown of glucose, so much less energy (about a twentieth) is released than in aerobic respiration.

**Lactic acid** is produced during anaerobic respiration. It is relatively **toxic** to the cells, and when it builds up in the muscles, it can cause pain (cramp) and a sensation of fatigue in the muscles.

$$glucose \longrightarrow lactic\ acid + small\ amount\ of\ energy\ released$$

(HT) During hard exercise there is a lack of oxygen in cells. Incomplete breakdown of glucose occurs. The lactic acid must be broken down quickly to avoid cell damage and relieve the feeling of fatigue.

Immediately after anaerobic exercise:
- **deep breathing continues**, so that oxygen is taken in to break down the lactic acid (producing carbon dioxide, water and more energy).
- the **heart rate stays high**, pumping blood through your muscles to remove the lactic acid and transport it to the liver to be broken down.

In effect, the body is taking in the oxygen that wasn't available for aerobic respiration during exertion. This is why the process is sometimes referred to as 'repaying the **oxygen debt**'.

**Key Words**    Aerobic respiration • Recovery rate • Anaerobic respiration • Lactic acid

## Multi-cell Organisms

Some simple organisms are unicellular, but more complex organisms are multicellular.

Multi-cell organisms (e.g. animals and humans) are **large** and **complex**.

The advantages of being multicellular include:

- allowing organisms to be larger
- allowing for cell differentiation
- allowing organisms to be complex.

(HT) Becoming multicellular requires the development of specialised organ systems for:

- communication between cells
- supplying the cells with nutrients
- controlling exchanges with the environment.

## Cells and Gametes

In mammals, most body cells are diploid which means that they contain two sets of matching chromosomes. But, some cells can be haploid which means they contain only one set of chromosomes.

**Gametes** are sex cells (eggs and sperm). They are specialised **haploid** cells. At fertilisation, gametes combine to form a **diploid zygote**. Genetic material from both parents combines to produce a unique individual. Genes on the chromosomes combine to control the characteristics of the zygote.

A **sperm** is a tiny cell with a tail which makes it very mobile. It contains many mitochondria to supply the energy needed for swimming.

On contact with the ovum, its **acrosome** (cap-like structure on its 'head') bursts. This releases enzymes that digest the egg cell's membrane, allowing the sperm nucleus, containing one set of chromosomes from the **father**, to enter. The surface of the egg then changes, making it impossible for other sperm to enter.

Sperm are produced and released in vast numbers because most die on the way so this increases the chance of fertilisation occurring.

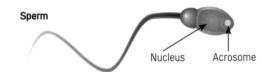

## Fertilisation

Fertilisation occurs during sexual reproduction. Two gametes (egg and sperm) fuse together.

Sexual reproduction in animals is the joining (fusing) of a sperm and an egg to produce a new, unique

individual. Half the genes come from each parent, as gametes have half the number of chromosomes of body cells.

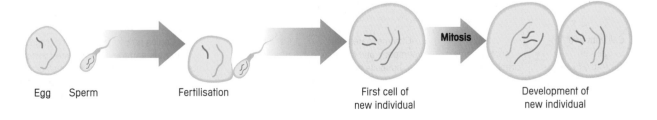

# B3 Cell Division

## Mitosis

New cells for growth are produced by **mitosis**. These cells are genetically identical. This type of cell division is needed for:

- the replacement of worn-out cells
- repair to damaged tissue
- asexual reproduction.

Before cells divide the DNA copies itself (DNA replication). This means the new cell will have a copy of all the chromosomes. Because there are no other parents involved and the DNA is copied, these cells are genetically identical.

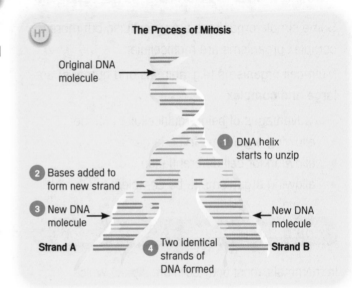

**(HT)** The Process of Mitosis

Original DNA molecule

1 DNA helix starts to unzip

2 Bases added to form new strand

3 New DNA molecule

New DNA molecule

**Strand A**

4 Two identical strands of DNA formed

**Strand B**

**(HT)** To copy itself, the DNA unzips to form single strands. New double strands form by **complementary base pairing**.

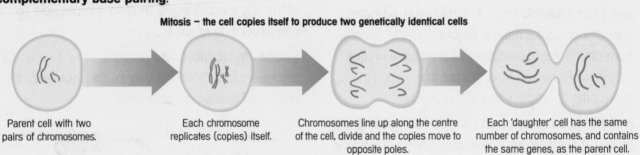

Mitosis – the cell copies itself to produce two genetically identical cells

| Parent cell with two pairs of chromosomes. | Each chromosome replicates (copies) itself. | Chromosomes line up along the centre of the cell, divide and the copies move to opposite poles. | Each 'daughter' cell has the same number of chromosomes, and contains the same genes, as the parent cell. |

## Meiosis

**Meiosis** is a type of cell division which occurs in the testes and ovaries. The cells in these organs divide to produce **gametes** for sexual reproduction.

The chromosome number is halved and each cell is genetically different. Meiosis introduces genetic **variation**.

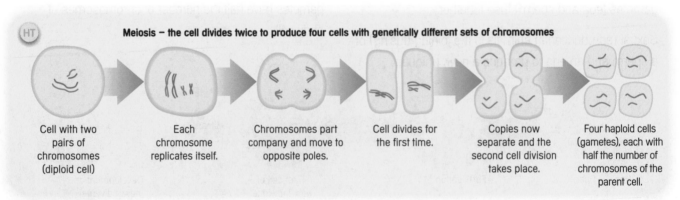

**(HT)** Meiosis – the cell divides twice to produce four cells with genetically different sets of chromosomes

| Cell with two pairs of chromosomes (diploid cell) | Each chromosome replicates itself. | Chromosomes part company and move to opposite poles. | Cell divides for the first time. | Copies now separate and the second cell division takes place. | Four haploid cells (gametes), each with half the number of chromosomes of the parent cell. |

## The Blood

Blood has **four** components – platelets (bits of broken cells), plasma, white blood cells and red blood cells.

**Platelets** clump together when a blood vessel becomes damaged in order to produce a **clot**.

**Plasma** transports several substances around the body including foods like glucose, water, hormones, antibodies and waste products.

**White blood cells** protect the body against disease. Some have a flexible shape which allows them to engulf disease-causing microorganisms.

**Red blood cells** transport oxygen from the lungs to the tissues. They:

- are small and flexible, so they can pass through narrow blood vessels
- don't have a nucleus, so they can be packed with **haemoglobin**.

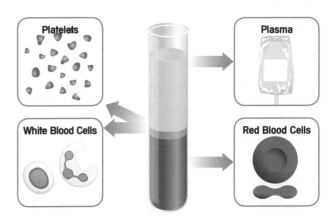

**HT** The small size and biconcave shape of red blood cells gives them a **large surface area to volume ratio** for absorbing oxygen. When the cells reach the lungs, oxygen diffuses from the lungs into the blood.

The haemoglobin molecules in the red blood cells bind with the oxygen to form oxyhaemoglobin.

$$\text{haemoglobin} + \text{oxygen} \longrightarrow \text{oxyhaemoglobin}$$

The blood is then pumped around the body to the tissues, where the reverse reaction takes place. Oxygen is released which diffuses into cells.

## The Circulatory System

Blood moves around the body in arteries, veins and capillaries:

- **Arteries** transport blood **away** from the **heart.**
- **Veins** transport blood **towards** the **heart.**
- **Capillaries** exchange materials with tissues.

The heart pumps blood around the body:

- The **right hand side** of the heart pumps blood which is low in oxygen **to the lungs and back.**
- The **left hand side** of the heart pumps blood which is rich in oxygen **to the rest of the body and back.**
- Blood pumped into the arteries is under much higher pressure than the blood in the veins.

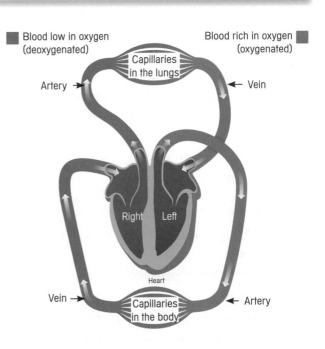

# B3 The Circulatory System

## The Circulatory System (Cont.)

Mammals have a **double circulatory system**, i.e. it consists of two loops. The advantage of this is that blood is pumped to the body at a higher pressure than it is pumped to the lungs. This provides a much greater rate of flow to the body tissues.

Arteries, veins and capillaries have special adaptations to help with their function:

- **Arteries** have to cope with a high pressure of blood so they have a **thick wall** made of **elastic muscle fibres**.

- **Veins** have a **lumen** which is much bigger compared to the thickness of the walls. They have **valves** to prevent the backflow of blood.
- **Capillaries** are the only blood vessels that have **thin permeable** walls, to allow the **exchange of substances** between cells and the blood.

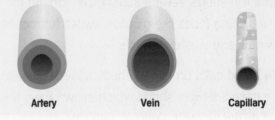

Artery      Vein      Capillary

## The Heart

Most of the wall of the heart is made of muscle. There are four main chambers:

- Left and right **ventricles**.
- Left and right **atria**.

**Ventricles** contract to pump blood out of the heart. The right ventricle pumps blood a short distance to the lungs. The left ventricle is **more muscular** because it pumps blood under **higher pressure** around the whole body, whereas the right ventricle only pumps blood to the lungs and back.

**Atria receive blood** coming back to the heart through the veins.

**Semilunar, tricuspid** and **bicuspid valves** make sure that the blood flows in the right direction (i.e. not backwards).

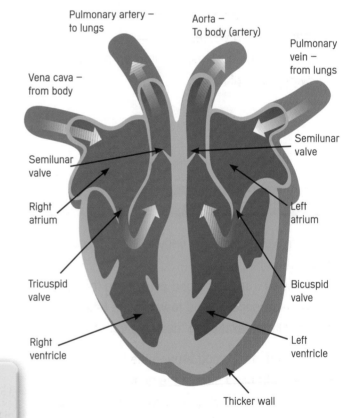

Pulmonary artery – to lungs

Aorta – To body (artery)

Pulmonary vein – from lungs

Vena cava – from body

Semilunar valve

Semilunar valve

Right atrium

Left atrium

Tricuspid valve

Bicuspid valve

Right ventricle

Left ventricle

Thicker wall

### Quick Test

1. Write the word equation for aerobic respiration.
2. What is produced during anaerobic respiration?
3. What are gametes?
4. In which organs does meiosis occur?
5. Name the four components of blood.
6. What does the pulmonary artery do?

## Plant Cells

Plant and animal cells contain a nucleus, cell membrane, and cytoplasm. Plant cells also contain **chloroplasts**, a **cellulose cell wall** to provide support and a **vacuole** which contains cell sap and helps to provide support.

Use this method to see the parts of a plant cell:

1. Use tweezers to peel a thin layer of skin tissue from an onion.
2. Place the onion tissue onto a microscope slide.
3. Add a drop of iodine to the tissue and carefully cover the slide with a coverslip.
4. Look at the onion cell through the microscope at ×100 magnification.

Bacterial cells are smaller and simpler than plant and animal cells. Bacterial cells lack a true nucleus. They also lack mitochondria and chloroplasts.

(HT) Plant cells keep their DNA inside the nucleus but bacterial cells have it floating as circular strands.

**Palisade Cell (Typical Plant Cell)**

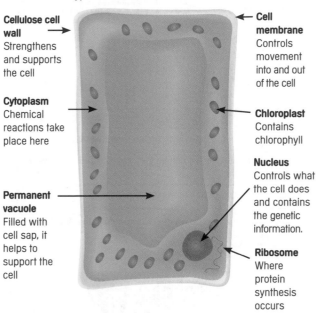

**Cellulose cell wall**
Strengthens and supports the cell

**Cytoplasm**
Chemical reactions take place here

**Permanent vacuole**
Filled with cell sap, it helps to support the cell

**Cell membrane**
Controls movement into and out of the cell

**Chloroplast**
Contains chlorophyll

**Nucleus**
Controls what the cell does and contains the genetic information.

**Ribosome**
Where protein synthesis occurs

*E. coli* – An Example of a Flagellate Bacillus

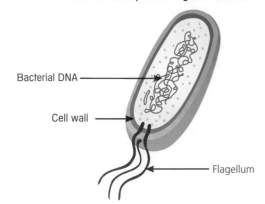

Bacterial DNA

Cell wall

Flagellum

## Growth

**Growth** is measured as an increase in height or mass. It involves both **cell division** and **cell differentiation**. Animals grow by increasing the number of cells. The cells **specialise** or **differentiate** into different types of cell at an early stage to form tissues and organs.

Animal cells lose the ability to differentiate at an early stage. Plant cells do not.

Animals grow in the early stages of their lives, and grow to a finite size. But, given the right conditions, many plants can grow continuously.

All parts of an animal are involved in growth whereas plants grow at specific parts of the plant.

Plant cell division is mainly restricted to areas called **meristems** at the roots and tips.

**Cell enlargement** is the main method by which plants gain height. Unlike animal cells, plant cells retain the ability to differentiate or specialise throughout their lives, whereas animals lose this ability at an early stage. In humans there are two phases of rapid growth: just after birth and during adolescence.

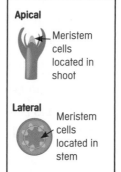

**Apical**
Meristem cells located in shoot

**Lateral**
Meristem cells located in stem

# B3 Growth and Development

## Growth (Cont.)

### Growth Curve

Graph 1 shows the main phases of a typical growth curve for a population. Graph 2 shows a typical growth curve for an individual.

### Measuring Growth

Growth can be measured as an increase in length/height, wet mass or dry mass. The best measure of growth is an increase in dry mass.

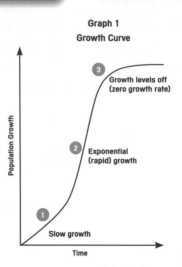

**Graph 1**
**Growth Curve**

3 Growth levels off (zero growth rate)

2 Exponential (rapid) growth

1 Slow growth

Population Growth

Time

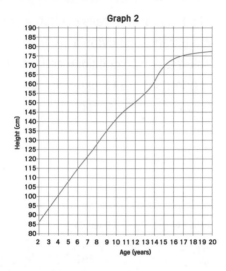

**Graph 2**

Height (cm)

Age (years)

(HT) The table below gives a summary of the different ways to measure growth.

| Method | Advantage | Disadvantage |
|---|---|---|
| Length/height | Easy and rapid measurement. | Increase in mass might occur with no increase in length/height. |
| Wet mass | Not destructive, is relatively easy to measure. | Water content of living tissue can be very variable and may give a distorted view overall. |
| Dry mass | Most accurate method. | Destructive as removal of water kills organism. |

The growth of different parts of an organism may differ from the growth rate of the whole organism. For example, in a human foetus the head and brain grow rapidly at first to coordinate the complex growth of the rest of the body.

**Stages of Development in the Womb**

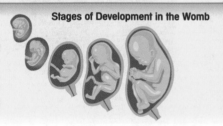

## Stem Cells

**Stem cells** are undifferentiated animal cells, which can specialise and develop into different types of cells, tissues and organs.

Stem cells can be obtained from embryonic tissue and scientists believe that they could potentially be used to treat medical conditions which presently have no cure.

For research, scientists need to obtain large numbers of embryos to grow the stem cells in the laboratory. At present, unused embryos from IVF (*in vitro* fertilisation) treatments are used.

Some people think that embryos left over from an IVF treatment would otherwise be destroyed, so it's a good use for them. The potential to cure disease is important. But others think that it's wrong to experiment on embryos – human life is sacred and shouldn't be experimented on. 'Playing God' is wrong and unnatural.

(HT) Embryonic stem cells can become any type of body cell, whereas adult stem cells are limited to differentiate into the cell types from their tissue of origin. So, embryonic stem cells have a much wider use.

## Selective Breeding

Animals or plants with favourable characteristics are **selected** and **deliberately crossbred** to produce offspring with the desired characteristics. This is **selective breeding**. These offspring can then also be selected and bred until the desired result is achieved. But, it can take many, many generations to get the desired results.

Selective breeding can contribute to **improved agricultural** yields in animals and crops. For example:

- **Quantity of milk** – cows have been selectively bred to produce **high volumes of milk** daily.
- **Quality of milk** – Jersey cows have been selectively bred to produce **rich** and **creamy milk**.
- **Beef production** – Some cattle have been selectively bred for characteristics such as hardiness, early maturity and high numbers of offspring.

Selective breeding may lead to in-breeding, which can cause health problems within a species.

(HT) There are risks and disadvantages to selective breeding. Intensive selective breeding reduces the gene pool, and the number of different **alleles** in the population decreases so there is **less variation**. Lack of variation can lead to an accumulation of harmful recessive characteristics (in-breeding).

**Example of Selective Breeding**

Choose the spottiest two to breed…

… and then the spottiest of their offspring…

… to eventually get Dalmatians.

## Genetic Engineering

All living organisms use the same basic genetic code (DNA), so, genes can be artificially transferred from one living organism to another. This process is called **genetic engineering** or **genetic modification** (**GM**). The transfer of genes can produce organisms with different characteristics.

Altering the genetic make-up of an organism can be done for many reasons:

- **To improve crop resistance** to frost damage, disease or herbicides, e.g. soya plants are genetically modified by inserting a gene that makes them resistant to a herbicide, so the plants can grow better without competition from weeds.
- **To improve the quality of food**, e.g. people who eat a diet mainly of rice may become deficient in Vitamin A. The genes responsible for producing beta-carotene (which the body converts into vitamin A) can be transferred from carrots to rice plants, so people can get beta-carotene from the genetically modified rice.
- **To produce a required substance**, e.g. the gene for human insulin can be inserted into bacteria to make insulin on a large scale to treat diabetes.

# B3 New Genes for Old

## Genetic Engineering (Cont.)

**Advantage of genetic engineering:**
- Allows organisms with new features to be produced rapidly.

**Disadvantage of genetic engineering:**
- The inserted genes may have **unexpected harmful effects**.

In the future it may be possible to use genetic engineering to change a person's genes and cure certain disorders.

### Ethical Considerations

Benefits of genetic engineering/modification include:
- producing disease-resistant crops and higher yields which could feed more of the world's population
- creating crops that will grow in poor or dry soil to feed people in poor areas

- potentially replacing faulty genes to reduce certain diseases.

But, there are concerns that:
- GM plants may cross-breed with wild plants and release their new genes into the environment
- GM foods may not be safe to eat in the long term
- it could lead to the genetic make-up of children being modified or engineered ('designer babies')
- unborn babies with genetic faults could be aborted
- insurance companies could genetically screen applicants and refuse to insure people who have an increased risk of illness.

## HT Principles of Genetic Engineering

1. The gene for a desired characteristic is **selected**, e.g. the human insulin gene.
2. The gene is **isolated** and removed using an enzyme which cuts through the DNA strands in precise places.
3. The selected gene is **inserted** into the genome of another organism, e.g. a bacterial cell.
4. When the organism **replicates**, the gene replicates making the new protein, e.g. human insulin.

## Gene Therapy

Changing a person's genes in an attempt to cure genetic disorders is called **gene therapy**.

HT Gene therapy can involve body cells or gametes. Gene therapy involving gametes (sex cells, sperm and egg) is very controversial. This is because the genetic changes that are made don't just affect the individual being treated but affect all future generations as those are the genes passed on to the offspring. The future generations don't have a say in the treatment and it may affect them, especially if it leads to problems.

### Quick Test

1. Name the process of producing organisms with desired characteristics through a breeding programme.
2. What is gene therapy?
3. How has genetic engineering helped people with diabetes?

## Asexual Reproduction

**Asexual reproduction** produces identical copies. Plants can reproduce asexually, i.e. in the absence of sex cells and fertilisation.

Spider plants, strawberry plants and potato plants all reproduce in this way.

**Spider Plant Stolons**

Stolon – a rooting side branch

New individual established

New individual (genetically identical) now independent

## Taking Cuttings

Plants grown from cuttings or tissue culture are **clones**. If a plant has desirable characteristics, it can be reproduced by taking stem, leaf or root cuttings.

1 Select a plant
2 Take cuttings
3 Place in damp atmosphere
4 New genetically identical plants develop

## Commercial Cloning of Plants

Plants can be cloned to be sold commercially. **Advantages** include:

- The cloned plants will be genetically identical to the parent, so all the characteristics will be known.
- It is possible to mass-produce plants that may be difficult to grow from seeds.

**Disadvantages** include:

- Any susceptibility to disease, or sensitivity to environmental conditions will affect all the plants.
- The reduction in **genetic variation** reduces the potential for further selective breeding.

## HT Cloning by Tissue Culture

Cloned plants can be produced by the following method:

1 Select a parent plant with desired characteristics.
2 Scrape off a lot of small pieces of tissue into beakers containing nutrients and hormones. Make sure that this process is done **aseptically** (without the presence of bacteria) to avoid the new plants rotting.
3 Lots of genetically identical plantlets will then grow (these can also be cloned).

Many older **plants** are still able to **differentiate** or **specialise**, whereas animal cells lose this ability. So, cloning plants is easier than cloning animals.

# B3 Cloning

## Cloning Animals

**Cloning** is an example of asexual reproduction which produces genetically identical copies. Identical twins are **naturally occurring** clones.

**Animals** can be **cloned artificially**. The most famous example is Dolly the sheep, who was the first mammal to be successfully cloned from an adult body cell.

A cloning technique called **embryo transplantation** is now commonly used in cattle breeding.

Dolly was produced by the process of **nuclear transfer**. This involved scientists placing the nucleus of a body cell (an udder cell) from the sheep they wanted to clone into an empty egg cell, which had had its nucleus removed. A short, sharp electric current helped the cell to start dividing. It was then implanted into another sheep to grow.

## Uses of Cloning

There are a number of uses of cloning:

- It's possible to clone human embryos in the same way that animals are cloned. This technique could be used to provide **stem cells** for medical purposes.
- The mass production of animals with desirable characteristics.
- Producing animals that have been genetically engineered to provide human products.

There are major ethical dilemmas about cloning humans:

- The cloning process is very unreliable – the majority of cloned embryos don't survive.
- Cloned animals seem to have a limited life span and die early.
- The effect of cloning on a human's mental and emotional development isn't known.
- Religious views say that cloning humans is wrong.
- Using human embryos and tampering with them is controversial.

## HT Adult Cell Cloning

The following method was used to produce a cloned sheep (i.e. Dolly):

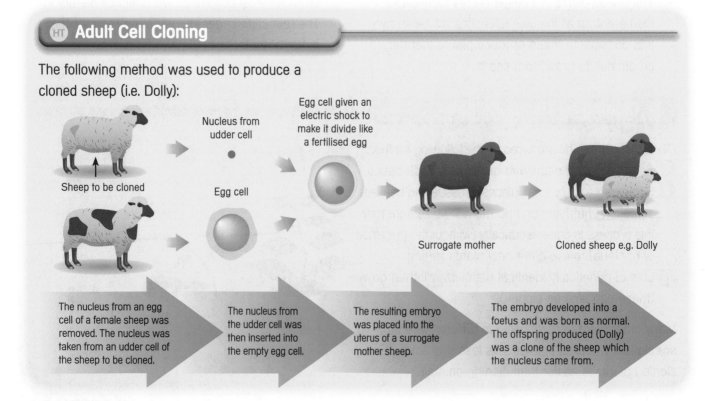

Sheep to be cloned

Nucleus from udder cell

Egg cell

Egg cell given an electric shock to make it divide like a fertilised egg

Surrogate mother

Cloned sheep e.g. Dolly

The nucleus from an egg cell of a female sheep was removed. The nucleus was taken from an udder cell of the sheep to be cloned.

The nucleus from the udder cell was then inserted into the empty egg cell.

The resulting embryo was placed into the uterus of a surrogate mother sheep.

The embryo developed into a foetus and was born as normal. The offspring produced (Dolly) was a clone of the sheep which the nucleus came from.

**Embryo • Stem cells**

## HT Benefits and Risks of Cloning

There are benefits and risks associated with cloning technology. **Benefits** include:

- Genetically identical cloned animals will all have the same characteristics.
- The sex of an animal and timing of birth can be controlled.
- Top-quality bulls and cows can be kept for egg and sperm donation, whilst other animals can be used to carry and give birth to the young.

**Risks** include:

- Cloning reduces genetic variation.
- Cloned animals are identical copies so they are all genetically the same. There is potential for one disease wiping them all out.
- Welfare concerns – cloned animals may not be as healthy or live as long as 'normal' animals.

## Animal Organ Donors

There is a **shortage** of **human organ donors** for **transplants**.

One possible solution would be to **genetically engineer** (i.e. artificially alter the genetic code of) an **animal** so its organs wouldn't be rejected by the human body. The animal could then be **cloned** to produce a ready supply of identical donor organs.

Animal organ donors could solve the problem of waiting lists for human transplants.
But, there are:

- concerns that infections might be passed from animals to humans
- ethical issues concerning animal welfare and rights.

## Quick Test

1. Give an example of naturally occurring clones in mammals.
2. What was the first mammal to be artificially cloned?
3. Suggest some possible uses for cloning.

# B3 Exam Practice Questions

**1** Look at this diagram of the human heart.

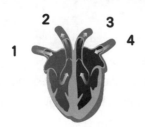

**a)** Name the four blood vessels labelled on the diagram.

1 = .........................     2 = .........................

3 = .........................     4 = .........................  **[4]**

**b)** What is the function of the valves? **[1]**

---

**2** The table shows the number of chromosomes in the body cells of a number of animals.

| Animal | No. of Chromosomes in Each Body Cell |
|---|---|
| Elephant | 56 |
| Tiger | 38 |
| Cat | 38 |
| Mouse | 40 |
| Carp | 104 |
| Snail | 24 |

**a)** How many chromosomes are in an elephant's sperm cell? **[1]**

**b)** How many chromosomes are in a mouse's skin cell? **[1]**

**c)** How does the number of chromosomes in a mouse's body cell compare to the number of chromosomes in a human body cell? **[1]**

---

**3** The table on the right charts Thomas's growth in mass from birth to age 2.

| Age (months) | 0 | 3 | 6 | 9 | 12 | 15 | 18 | 21 | 24 |
|---|---|---|---|---|---|---|---|---|---|
| Mass (kg) | 2.8 | 4.9 | 6.3 | 7.4 | 9.0 | 9.7 | 10.0 | 10.3 | 10.6 |

The graphs show the growth rates of two other babies: Gabriel and Finn. Gabriel had no health problems from birth to age 2, but Finn did show health problems.

**a)** Plot a graph of Thomas's growth data and create a growth curve. **[4]**

**b)** Between which ages did Thomas grow fastest? **[1]**

**c)** What can you conclude about Thomas's growth from studying the graph? **[1]**

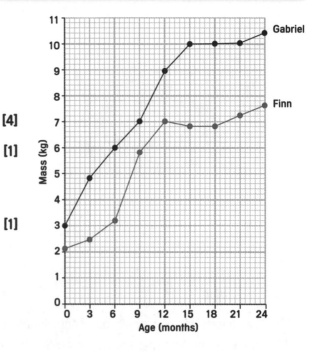

**4** The diagram shows the cloning technique that was used to produce Dolly the sheep.

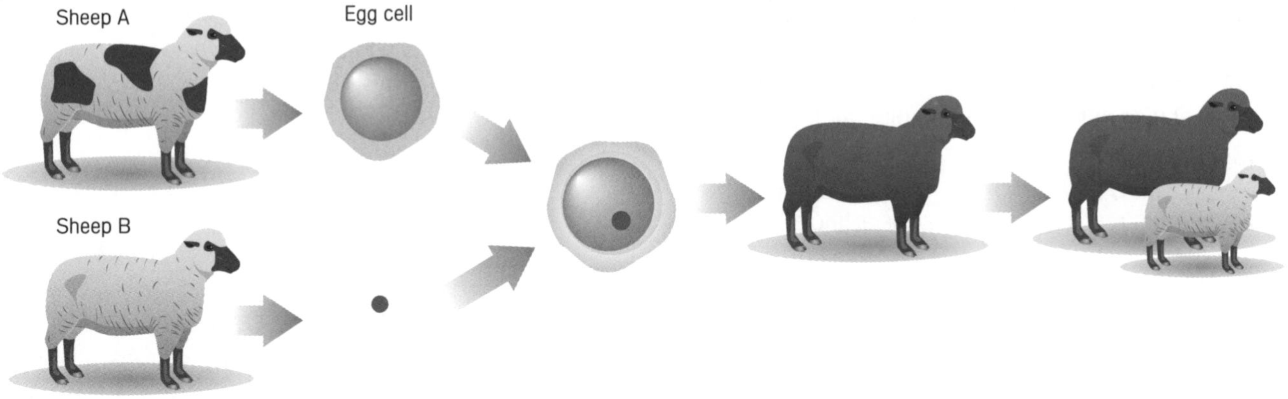

Sheep A    Egg cell

Sheep B

**a)** What is a clone? _____ **[1]**

**b)** Some people do not like the idea of cloning animals. Suggest two reasons why you think this is. **[2]**

_____

_____

**c)** In nature, give an example you often see of natural clones. _____ **[1]**

**HT d)** Describe, with the help of the diagram, the cloning technique shown in the diagram. **[3]**

_____

_____

_____

**e)** Is Dolly a clone of sheep A or B? Without referring to the sheep's colour, explain your answer. **[1]**

_____

_____

**5 a)** The sequence of bases in DNA determines the order of amino acids in a protein. Here is a sequence of bases for a section of DNA.

**A G C T G C T G A C T A**

How many amino acids are coded for by this section of DNA? **[1]**

_____

**b)** Complete the DNA molecule by adding the correct base to each strand. **[2]**

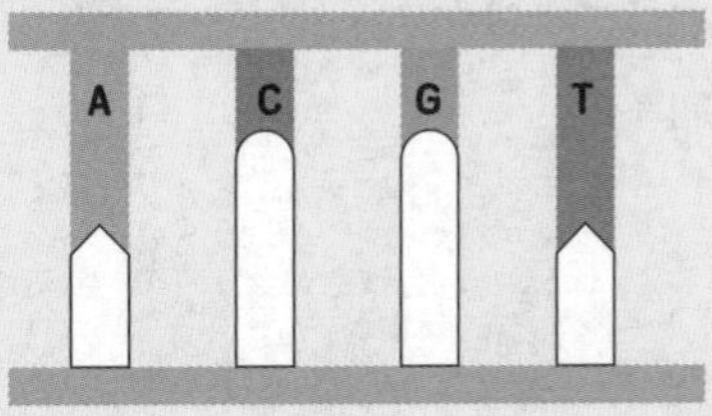

A    C    G    T

# B4 Ecology in the Local Environment

## Ecosystems

An **ecosystem** is a physical environment with a particular set of conditions, plus all the organisms that live in it.

An ecosystem can be natural or artificial.

(HT) **Natural** ecosystems have high **biodiversity**, i.e. many different species of plants and animals **coexist** in the same environment.

**Artificial** ecosystems, for example, greenhouses, are designed and maintained for a particular **purpose** so they have lower biodiversity.

**Weedkillers**, **fertilisers** and **pesticides** may be used in artificial ecosystems to prevent other animals and plants from growing alongside the crop. This leads to low biodiversity.

**Forestry plantations** are very carefully set up, controlled and monitored. They will have less biodiversity due to the fact they haven't been established for as long as natural woodland, which take years to form, and result from the relationships and interactions of the organisms that live there and their surroundings. Fewer species are introduced at the setting up stage and not all species survive from the start.

**Fish farms** will also show less biodiversity due to the shorter time they have existed compared to lakes. Plus in the absence of many predators some fish species will thrive while others will not. Also there are fewer diseases which may result in too many of certain species reducing others.

## Ecological Terms

A **habitat** is the part of the physical environment where an animal or plant lives. An organism will have adapted to its habitat, so it may be restricted to living there. It may only eat the food there.

A **community** is the total number of individuals of all the different populations of plants and animals that live together in a habitat at any one time.

A **population** is the total number of individuals of the same species that live in a certain area.

(HT) Ecosystems are self supporting in all factors, e.g. providing mates, shelter, but the one thing they all rely on is an energy source (the Sun) and producers at the bottom of the food chain.

## Sampling Methods

The size and distribution of a population can be measured by using one or more of the following techniques: pooters, sweepnets, pitfall traps or quadrats.

**Pooters** are containers used to collect insects easily, without harming them.

**Sweepnets** are used to collect insects in long grass or moderately dense woodland where there are lots of shrubs.

**Pitfall traps** are containers set into the ground that are used to catch small insects, e.g. beetles.

**Quadrats** are square frames that have sides usually 0.5 m long. They are used to count a smaller, representative part of a population. You should throw them randomly on the ground, then count and record the number of each species within the quadrat. You can then estimate the population of each species in a given area. Quadrat sizes can vary depending on the area you're surveying.

For example, Noah randomly threw 10 quadrats (each quadrat was 0.25 m²) on the school picnic area. He found a total of 2 buttercup plants. So, in 2.5 m² Noah found 2 buttercup plants. The picnic area was 25 m² so **scaling up** would make 20 buttercups on the picnic area. Scaling up is great for estimating a population from a small sample area. It's important that the throws are random.

(HT) When **sampling**, you must make sure you:
- take a **big enough** sample to make the results a **good estimate** – the larger the sample the more accurate the results
- sample **randomly** – the more random the sample the more likely it is to be **representative** of the population.

In a habitat, organisms are distributed at random.

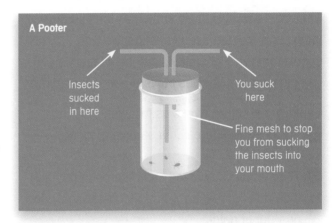

A Pooter

Insects sucked in here

You suck here

Fine mesh to stop you from sucking the insects into your mouth

A Sweepnet

A Pitfall Trap

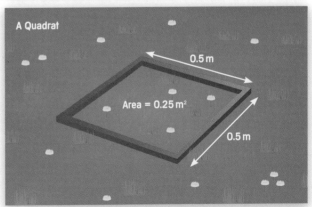

A Quadrat

0.5 m

Area = 0.25 m²

0.5 m

# B4 Ecology in the Local Environment

## Capture–Recapture

**Capture–recapture** (also known as the **Lincoln Index**) is a method used to estimate a population size. Populations can be difficult to sample because species move around all the time.

Capture–recapture works as follows:

1. A trap is used to catch a sample of individuals, e.g. mice.
2. The sample is counted and recorded and each individual is marked with a numbered tag/band or a dot of paint.
3. The individuals are released unharmed back into the environment, and are given time to redistribute themselves among the unmarked population.
4. Another sample of individuals is captured. Some of them are already marked and some are unmarked.
5. The unmarked animals are counted and recorded. They are then marked and released.

This formula can then be used to estimate the total population size in the habitat:

$$\text{Population size} = \frac{\text{No. in 1}^{st}\text{ sample (all marked)} \times \text{no. in 2}^{nd}\text{ sample (marked and unmarked)}}{\text{No. in 2}^{nd}\text{ sample which were previously marked}}$$

(HT) When you use this method you have to:
- assume that no organisms have died, immigrated or emigrated between sampling
- make sure that identical sampling methods are used from one visit to the next
- make sure that marking the organisms doesn't affect their survival, e.g. be careful when using paint on invertebrates because if too much is used it can enter their respiratory passages and kill them.

The larger the sample size, the more accurate the population size estimate.

## Using Transects

A **transect** line is used to map the distribution of organisms. It is used for studies of how species change across a boundary between habitats, e.g. a rocky shoreline.

1. A line like a tape measure is laid out.
2. Quadrats are distributed in regular intervals on the line, and the species in the quadrats are counted.

Counting the animals and plants in quadrats along the line of a transect gives a lot of numbers, making it difficult to see trends and compare different parts of the habitat. So the data is presented as a **kite diagram**.

## Kite Diagrams

You can create a kite diagram by doing the following:

1. Use graph paper and begin by drawing a sketch of the habitat profile across the bottom to scale.
2. Draw a horizontal line above this and locate the quadrats – mark a vertical bar at each quadrat location (use 5 squares above and 5 below for Abundant, 4 for Common, 3 for Some, 2 for Few, 1 for only one).
3. Join the tops and bottoms of these bars. 'Not present' will be a point on the horizontal line, so the diagram that results will have a shape something like a kite. That is the profile and one species done.
4. Do the same for the next species, and so on.

Remember the presence or absence plus abundance of an organism is affected by other organisms in the area, e.g. predators, as well as other physical factors like the tides or water temperature.

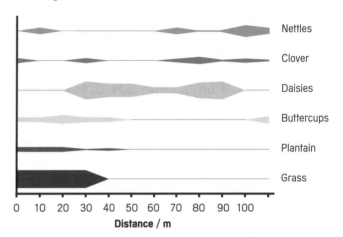

Kite Diagram of Woodland Habitat

HT Kite diagrams show zonation. Zonation is the gradual change in the distribution of species across a habitat. Gradual changes in abiotic factors (non-living factors), e.g. tides, water temperature, salinity of a rock pool, can result in zonation of organisms in a habitat. This is clearly seen in rocky shores where there are distinct zones of organisms due to the changing tides and the different conditions created.

In the example alongside, zonation of the mussels and periwinkles is directly affected by water level.

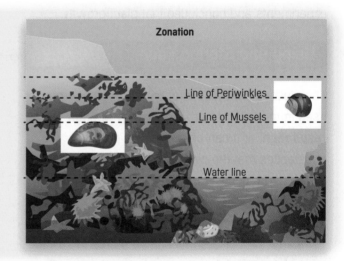

Zonation

## Keys

Correctly identifying species in a sample can be hard. Using keys can help to identify organisms correctly.

Here is an example of a simple key.

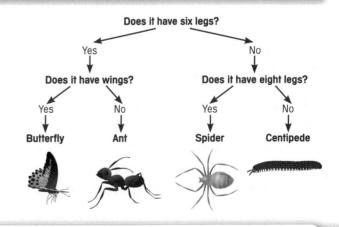

# B4 Photosynthesis

## Photosynthesis

Green **plants** make their own **food** (glucose and starch), using **sunlight**. This is called **photosynthesis**.

Photosynthesis produces **glucose** for biomass and energy. **Oxygen** is released as a by-product. The equation for photosynthesis is as follows:

$$\text{carbon dioxide} + \text{water} \xrightarrow[\text{chlorophyll}]{\text{light energy}} \text{glucose} + \text{oxygen}$$

$$6CO_2 + 6H_2O \longrightarrow C_6H_{12}O_6 + 6O_2$$

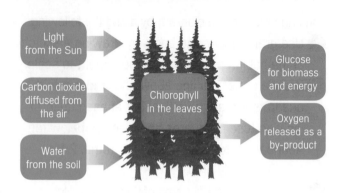

## Understanding Photosynthesis

How we understand photosynthesis has changed and evolved over time. The Greek scientists thought that plants gained mass only by taking in minerals from the soil. **Van Helmont** carried out many experiments and concluded that plant growth cannot be due only to the nutrients in the soil.

**Joseph Priestley** put a plant in a jar of air, and a plant in a jar with a mouse inside. He changed the combinations of plants and mouse and concluded that oxygen is produced by plants.

## Using and Storing Food

The glucose produced in photosynthesis can be used immediately to produce energy through **respiration**, or it can be **converted** into other substances that the plant needs. Glucose and starch can be converted into:

* **energy** (during respiration)
* proteins for **growth** and **repair**
* starch, fats or oils that can be **stored** in seeds
* cellulose, which is needed for plant **cell walls**.

**Glucose** is **soluble**. It can be **transported** around the plant as soluble sugar, but it must be converted into **starch**, which is **insoluble**, in order to be **stored**.

(HT) Starch is a very useful storage molecule. It is insoluble so it doesn't affect the water **concentration** inside the cells where it's stored. It also does not move away in solution from storage areas. If the cells stored soluble glucose, the inside of the cells would become very concentrated and water would constantly **move** in through osmosis, which would make the cell **swell**.

## (HT) The Chemistry of Photosynthesis

Using radioactive oxygen-18, scientists discovered that the oxygen produced as a by-product in photosynthesis comes from the water and not the carbon dioxide. Only when oxygen-18 is introduced via the water do you get a radioactive waste product of oxygen. This shows that photosynthesis is a two-stage process. Firstly, light energy is used to split water, releasing oxygen gas and hydrogen ions. Secondly, the carbon dioxide gas combines with the hydrogen (ions) to make glucose.

**Key Words**     Photosynthesis • Glucose • Soluble • Insoluble

## Increasing Photosynthesis

Plants need **light** and **warmth** to grow. This is why they grow faster in the summer.

Photosynthesis can be **increased** by increasing:

* the **temperature** – using heaters in a greenhouse
* the **light intensity** – using lamps in a greenhouse
* the **carbon dioxide** ($CO_2$) **concentration** – using chemicals, or as a by-product of using gas heaters in a greenhouse.

### Quick Test

1. Name four methods of collecting/counting organisms.
2. How is the data from a transect usually presented?
3. What is glucose stored as in plants?
4. How can the rate of photosynthesis be increased?

(HT) As the **temperature** rises, so does the rate of photosynthesis. This means temperature is the limiting factor in the rate of photosynthesis. As the temperature approaches 45°C, the enzymes controlling photosynthesis start to be denatured and the rate of photosynthesis declines to zero.

As the **carbon dioxide concentration** rises, so does the rate of photosynthesis. So carbon dioxide is limiting the rate of photosynthesis, up to a certain point. After this point, a rise in carbon dioxide levels has no effect. So, carbon dioxide is no longer the limiting factor; light or temperature must be.

As the **light intensity** increases, so does the rate of photosynthesis. This means light intensity is limiting the rate of photosynthesis up to a certain point. After this point, a rise in light intensity has no effect. Light intensity is no longer the limiting factor; carbon dioxide or temperature must be.

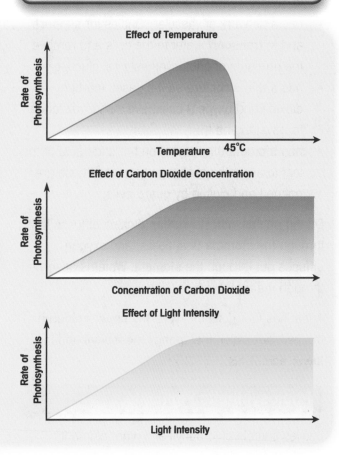

## Respiration in Plants

Plants **respire** to break down glucose to release **energy**. They respire all the time, i.e. day and night.

(HT) During the **day**, light is available from the Sun so plants **photosynthesise**; taking in carbon dioxide to make glucose and releasing oxygen as a by-product.

During the **day** and **night**, they **respire**, absorbing oxygen and giving out carbon dioxide. Respiration is the reverse of photosynthesis. Plants photosynthesise much faster than they respire when light is available. This is why they give out oxygen during the day.

# B4 Leaves and Photosynthesis

## Plant Leaves

**Photosynthesis** occurs mainly in the leaves of plants. Leaves are specially adapted for efficiency. For example, a leaf:

- contains a pigment **chlorophyll** (which absorbs light) in millions of chloroplasts, plus other pigments to absorb light from different parts of the spectrum
- is **broad** and **flat** to provide a **huge surface area** to absorb sunlight
- has a network of vascular bundles for **support**, and to **transport** water to the cells and remove the products of photosynthesis, i.e. glucose
- has a **thin structure** so the gases (carbon dioxide and oxygen) only have a short distance to travel to and from the cells
- has **stomata** (tiny pores) on the underside of the leaf to allow the **exchange** of **gases**; these are opened and closed by **guard cells**.

During photosynthesis **carbon dioxide** diffuses in through the **stomata** (leaf pores) and **oxygen** diffuses out through the **stomata**. Water is absorbed through the roots.

A leaf has four distinct layers: the **upper epidermis**, the **palisade layer**, the **spongy mesophyll** and the **lower epidermis**.

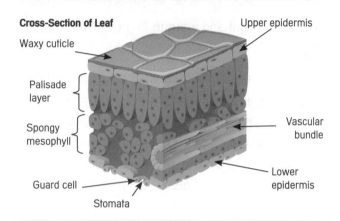

Cross-Section of Leaf

Waxy cuticle — Upper epidermis — Palisade layer — Spongy mesophyll — Vascular bundle — Guard cell — Lower epidermis — Stomata

**HT** In a typical leaf:
- the **upper epidermis** is **transparent** to allow sunlight through to the layer below
- the **cells** in the **palisade layer** are near the **top** of the leaf and are packed with **chloroplasts** so they can absorb the maximum amount of light
- the **spongy mesophyll** contains lots of **air spaces** connected to the stomata to allow the optimum exchange of gases.

This internal structure provides a **very large surface area** to **volume ratio** for efficient gaseous exchange.

Plant cells contain many chloroplasts and are long so they can absorb lots of light. Chloroplasts are not found in all plant cells, for example, root cells don't have chloroplasts as they obviously don't receive any light.

## Photosynthetic Pigments

Leaves contain chlorophyll and other pigments which absorb different wavelengths of light.

**HT** Chlorophyll is a mixture of pigments including chlorophyll a, chlorophyll b, xanthophylls and carotene. This chart shows that when lights of different colours are shone on chlorophyll a and b, they absorb different ranges of colours, but both tend to absorb colours in the red and violet ends of the spectrum. When lights of different colours are shone on a plant and the rate of photosynthesis is measured, the maximum rates are obtained in the red and violet ends too. The greener colours are reflected, which is why plants tend to be green.

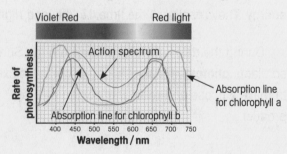

Violet Red — Red light — Action spectrum — Rate of photosynthesis — Absorption line for chlorophyll a — Absorption line for chlorophyll b — Wavelength / nm — 400 450 500 550 600 650 700 750

## Diffusion

Substances move in and out of cell membranes by **diffusion**. **Diffusion** is the movement of a substance from a region of **high concentration** to a region of **low concentration**.

Particles move about in lots of different directions. This is called **random movement**. Diffusion is the **net (overall) movement** of particles from an area of high concentration to an area of low concentration.

(HT) The **rate** of **diffusion** is increased when:
- there's a greater surface area of the cell membrane
- there's a greater difference between concentrations (a steeper concentration gradient)
- the particles have a shorter distance to travel.

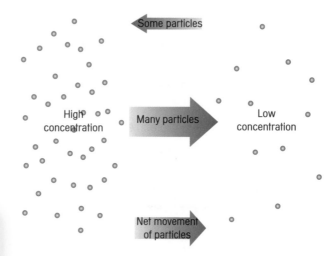

## Diffusion in Plants

Carbon dioxide ($CO_2$) and oxygen ($O_2$) move in and out of plants through their leaves.

During the day:
- **carbon dioxide** is used up in **photosynthesis**. The concentration inside the leaves is lower than the concentration outside the leaves.
- carbon dioxide diffuses into plants through the stomata (tiny pores) on the bottom of their leaves
- oxygen, a product of photosynthesis, diffuses from the plant into the atmosphere.

At **night**, photosynthesis stops. Oxygen diffuses **into** leaf cells and carbon dioxide diffuses **out of** leaf cells.

The **stomata** on the underside of leaves are specially adapted to:
- **open** – to help increase the rate of diffusion of carbon dioxide and oxygen
- **close** – to prevent excessive water loss in drought conditions.

**Magnified Cross-section of Leaf**

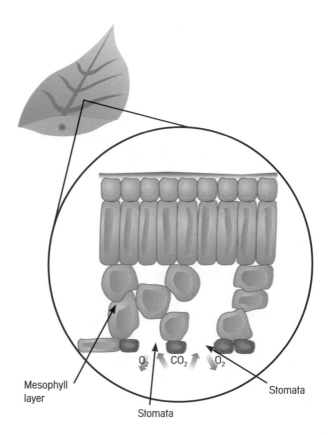

# B4 Diffusion and Osmosis

## Osmosis

**Osmosis** is the **diffusion** of water **from high concentration of water** (dilute solution) **to low concentration of water** (concentrated solution) through a **partially-permeable membrane** (a membrane that allows the passage of water molecules but not solute molecules). Osmosis is a special type of diffusion involving water molecules.

Plant cells are surrounded by a **membrane** which allows water to move in and out of the cells. Water and solute molecules move freely through the cellulose cell wall. The function of the cell wall is to provide support – it doesn't affect the movement of substances in or out of the cell.

## HT Net Movement

In osmosis, the water particles move randomly, colliding with each other and passing through the membrane in both directions. But, the **net movement** of molecules is from the area of high water concentration to the area of low water concentration. This gradually **dilutes** the solution.

You can **predict the direction** of water movement if you know what the **concentration** of the water is. Remember, solute molecules can't pass through the membrane; only the water molecules can.

Movement of water is always from high to low water concentration.

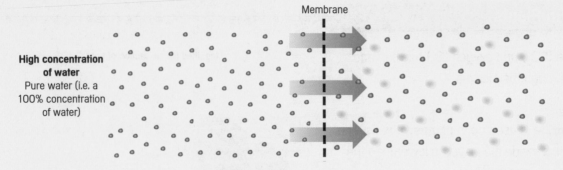

Membrane

**High concentration of water**
Pure water (i.e. a 100% concentration of water)

**Low concentration of water**
Sugar dissolved in water, (i.e. less than a 100% concentration of water)

## Osmosis in Animal Cells

Water also diffuses in and out of animal cells through the cell membrane by **osmosis**. But, animal cells don't have a cell wall, so too much water entering a cell could cause the cell to burst.

**Example – Red blood cells**

1 When red blood cells are in solutions with the same concentration as their cytoplasm, they retain their shape.

2 When in a weaker solution, they absorb water, swell up, and may burst.

3 When in a more concentrated solution, they lose water and shrivel up.

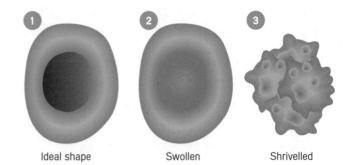

Ideal shape    Swollen    Shrivelled

## HT Osmosis in Animal Cells (Cont.)

**Animal cells**, unlike plant cells, **don't have an inelastic cell wall**.

Blood cells in a pure water solution will gain water by osmosis. Without a cell wall to prevent water entering the cell, they absorb more and more water until eventually they burst. This is called **lysis**.

Blood cells in a concentrated solution (very little water) will lose water by osmosis. Without a cell wall to prevent water loss, they can shrivel up and become **crenated** (have rough edges).

## Osmosis in Plant Cells

**Plant cells** have **inelastic cell walls** which, together with the **water inside the cells**, are essential for the **support** of young non-woody plants. The cell wall:

- prevents cells from bursting due to excess water
- contributes to rigidity.

The pressure of the water pushing against the cell wall is called **turgor pressure**.

A lack of water can cause plants to **droop** (**wilt**). As the amount of water inside the cells reduces, the cells become less rigid due to reduced turgor pressure.

HT As water moves into plant cells **by osmosis**, the **pressure inside the cell increases**. The inelastic cell walls can withstand the pressure and the cell becomes very turgid (rigid). When all the cells are fully turgid, the plant is firm and upright. But, if water is in short supply, cells will start to lose water **by osmosis**. They lose turgor pressure and become flaccid (not rigid), and the plant begins to wilt.

When cells lose a lot of water, the inside of the cell contracts. This is called plasmolysis.

Rigid Plant

Wilting Plant

## Quick Test

1. How do gases get in and out of a leaf?
2. Where are stomata found?
3. Which plant cells don't have any chloroplasts?
4. Explain what turgor pressure is and why it's important.

**Key Words**     Turgid • Flaccid • Plasmolysis

# B4 Transport in Plants

## Vascular Bundles

The **xylem** and **phloem** form a continuous system of tubes from roots to leaves, called **vascular bundles**.

- **Xylem** transports water and soluble mineral salts from the roots to the leaves (transpiration).
- **Phloem** allows the movement of food substances (sugars) around the plant (translocation), up and down stems to growing tissues and storage tissues.

(HT) **Xylem vessels** are made from dead plant cells. They have a hollow lumen. The cellulose cell walls are thickened with a waterproof substance. **Phloem** cells are long columns of living cells.

Root hairs have an enormous surface area for absorbing water and so increase the plant's ability to take up water.

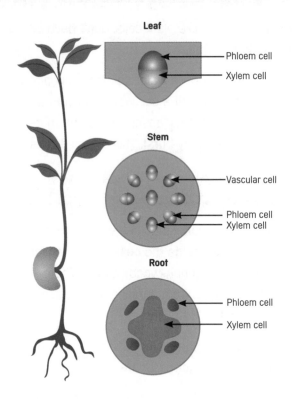

Leaf — Phloem cell, Xylem cell

Stem — Vascular cell, Phloem cell, Xylem cell

Root — Phloem cell, Xylem cell

## Transpiration

**Transpiration** is the **diffusion** and **evaporation** of water from inside a leaf. It causes water to be moved up xylem vessels and provides plants with water for cooling, photosynthesis and support, and brings minerals to the plant.

The transpiration stream is powered by the evaporation of water from the leaf:

1. Water evaporates from the internal leaf cells through the stomata.
2. Water passes by osmosis from the xylem vessels to leaf cells, which pull the thread of water in that vessel upwards by a very small amount.
3. Water enters the xylem from root tissues, to replace water which has moved upwards.
4. Water enters root hair cells by osmosis to replace water which has entered the xylem.

The rate of **transpiration** can be affected by:

- **light** – more light increases the rate of photosynthesis and transpiration

- **air movement (wind)** – as the movement of the air increases, transpiration increases
- **temperature** – heat increases the rate of photosynthesis and transpiration
- **humidity** – low humidity increases the rate of transpiration.

A leafy shoot's rate of transpiration can be measured using a **mass potometer**.

1. The plant's roots are submerged in a sealed bag of water and placed in a beaker.
2. The beaker is placed on a digital balance.
3. Readings are then taken to see how much water is lost by the plant during transpiration.
4. The conditions, e.g. light, temperature, can be changed to see how this affects water loss.

**Key Words** Transpiration • Translocation • Evaporation

## Water in Plants

Healthy plants need to balance the amount of water they take in and lose:

1. Water is **absorbed** by the plant by the root hair cells, which have a large surface area to take in water.
2. The water then diffuses through the plant up to the leaves.
3. When it reaches the leaves it can be lost by **transpiration** (evaporation).

Two **adaptations** reduce the rate at which water is lost from leaves:

- A **waxy cuticle** on the surface of the leaf.
- Having the majority of the **stomata** on the **lower surface** of the leaf.

## Quick Test

1. What factors affect the rate of transpiration?
2. What is the role of transpiration?
3. HT Describe the structures of the xylem and phloem.

## HT Water Loss from Leaves

**Transpiration** and **water loss** are an unavoidable consequence of photosynthesis. Although **stomata** are **needed** for the **exchange of gases** during photosynthesis, they also allow water molecules to pass out of the leaf. But, the **leaf** is **adapted** to be able to **reduce** water loss:

- The **number**, **position**, **size** and **distribution** of stomata vary between plants, depending on their environment (which affects the amount of water they need).
- The **turgidity** of guard cells changes in relation to the **light intensity** and **availability** of water, in order to alter the size of the stomatal openings.

During photosynthesis, the **guard cells** become **turgid** and the stomata are fully open. But, if there is a lack of water, the guard cells become **flaccid** and the stomata close to prevent unnecessary water loss and photosynthesis. Transpiration rate is affected by:

- **High light intensity** which causes the stomata to open – this increases the rate of water evaporation.

- **High temperatures** which increase the movement of the water molecules – this speeds up transpiration.
- **Increased air movement** which blows the water molecules away from stomata – this increases transpiration.
- **High humidity** which decreases the concentration gradient – this slows down transpiration.

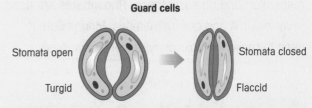

Guard cells

Stomata open — Turgid — Stomata closed — Flaccid

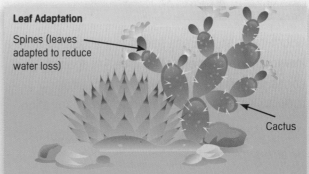

**Leaf Adaptation**

Spines (leaves adapted to reduce water loss)

Cactus

# B4 Plants Need Minerals

## Essential Minerals

**Essential minerals** are needed to keep plants healthy and growing properly. Plants absorb dissolved minerals in the soil through their roots.

The minerals are **naturally present** in the soil, although usually in quite **low concentrations**. So, farmers use fertilisers containing essential minerals e.g. (NPK) to make sure that plants get all the minerals they need to grow.

Each mineral is needed for a different purpose:
- **nitrates (N)** – to make proteins for cell growth
- **potassium compounds (K)** – for respiration and photosynthesis
- **phosphates (P)** – for respiration and cell growth
- **magnesium** – for photosynthesis.

If one or more of the essential minerals is missing (deficient) from the soil, the growth of the plant will be affected.

Experiments can be carried out to see how removing one mineral affects the plants. This is done by growing plants in a soil-less culture. The minerals can then be carefully controlled and changed.

(HT) **Nitrates** are used to make amino acids that form proteins. **Potassium** is used to help the enzymes in respiration and photosynthesis. **Phosphates** are used to make DNA and cell membranes. **Magnesium** is used to make the chlorophyll for photosynthesis.

**Lack of Nitrates**
Poor growth, yellow leaves

**Lack of Potassium**
Poor flower and fruit growth, discoloured leaves

**Lack of Phosphates**
Poor root growth, discoloured leaves

**Lack of Magnesium**
Yellow leaves

## (HT) Active Transport

Substances sometimes need to be absorbed from a **low** to a **high concentration** area, i.e. against a concentration gradient. This is called active transport and it requires **energy** from **respiration**.

Plants absorb mineral ions through their root hairs by active transport.

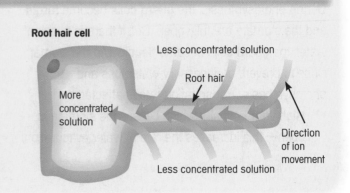

**Root hair cell**

Less concentrated solution

Root hair

More concentrated solution

Direction of ion movement

Less concentrated solution

Fertiliser • Active transport

## Decay

Decay is a process involving the breakdown of complex substances into simpler ones by microorganisms. The key factors in the process of decay are microbes, temperature, oxygen and moisture.

The rate of decay is affected by several factors:

- Changing **temperature** – microorganisms responsible for decay work best at around 40°C.
- **Amount of oxygen** – microorganisms' rate of activity increases as the amount of oxygen in the air increases.
- **Amount of water** – microorganisms prefer moist conditions.

(HT) **Temperature** – microorganisms work slowly at low temperatures, but at high temperatures (above 40°C) their enzymes are denatured and decay stops.

**Amount of oxygen** – increasing the amount of oxygen increases the microorganisms' rate of respiration, which means they produce more energy, enabling them to grow and reproduce more quickly. The more oxygen there is, the faster they grow.

**Amount of water** – microorganisms grow quickest in moist conditions. Too much or too little water will slow down their growth and, therefore, the rate of decay.

## Decomposers

**Earthworms, woodlice and maggots** are known as detritivores. They feed on:

- dead organisms
- decaying material (detritus) produced by living organisms.

Detritivores speed up the process of decay by breaking down detritus into small particles which have a large surface area. This makes it easier for decomposers (bacteria and fungi) to feed on.

Microorganisms are used to break down:

- human waste in sewage treatment works
- plant waste in compost heaps.

Materials that can decay can be recycled because decaying materials release minerals back into the soil. Plants use these minerals to grow.

(HT) Fungi are saprophytes – they feed on dead organic material by secreting **enzymes** onto the material and then absorbing the digested products. Saprophytes are essential for decay.

**A Garden Composter**

# B4 Decay

## Food Preservation

Food can be preserved by removing the **oxygen**, **warmth** or **moisture** (water) that the **microorganisms** need in order to grow or survive. Food can be:

- sealed inside sterile cans (canning) – this prevents entry of **decomposers**
- kept at **low temperatures** in a fridge or freezer – this slows down reproduction of the microorganisms' growth
- **pickled** in vinegar – acid kills the decomposers
- **preserved** in sugar (or salt) – this removes water from the decomposers by **osmosis**, so killing them.
- **dried** – this reduces the water.

All these methods reduce the rate of **decay**.

## Food Preservation Experiment

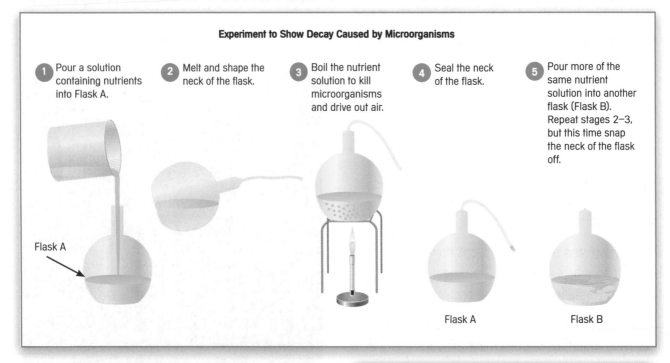

**Experiment to Show Decay Caused by Microorganisms**

1. Pour a solution containing nutrients into Flask A.
2. Melt and shape the neck of the flask.
3. Boil the nutrient solution to kill microorganisms and drive out air.
4. Seal the neck of the flask.
5. Pour more of the same nutrient solution into another flask (Flask B). Repeat stages 2–3, but this time snap the neck of the flask off.

Flask A

Flask A    Flask B

The solution in the flask that had the neck snapped off (Flask B) will start to decay within days because microorganisms will be able to enter the flask.

But, the solution in the other flask (Flask A) will show no signs of decay as long as it remains sealed.

## Quick Test

1. What does NPK stand for?
2. If a plant lacks nitrates how will it be affected?
3. What is needed for decay?
4. Name six food preservation techniques.

Microorganism • Decomposers • Osmosis

## Intensive Farming

**Intensive farming** methods aim to produce as much food as possible from the available land, plants and animals. These methods use chemicals like **pesticides** to kill pests that damage crops or livestock so more food is produced:

- **Pesticides** – used to kill pests i.e. any organism that can damage crops or farm animals.
- **Insecticides** (types of pesticide) – used to kill insect pests.
- **Fungicides** (types of pesticide) – used to kill fungi.
- **Herbicides** – used to kill weeds which compete with crops for water and nutrients.

But, care needs to be taken with pesticides because:
- they can harm other organisms (non-pests)
- they can build up (accumulate) in food chains, harming animals at the top.
- some pesticides are persistent – they stay in the food chain for years.

Intensive farming can **increase productivity** by keeping animals in carefully controlled environments where their temperature is controlled and movement is very limited. For example:
- battery farming
- glasshouses
- hydroponics
- fish farming.

But, this can raise **ethical dilemmas**. Some people find this **morally unacceptable** because the animals have a very poor quality of life.

(HT) Keeping animals warm and penned up inside (battery farming) so that they can't move improves the energy transfer by reducing the amount of energy lost at each stage of the food chain. But it's very cruel to the hens as they are kept in such small, confined spaces, and suffer health problems as a result.

By reducing energy transfer to pests, intensive farming improves the efficiency of energy transfer in food chains.

Intensive Farming

Use of Pesticides

# B4 Farming

## Organic Farming

**Organic farming** methods aim to produce food without the use of chemicals, so minimising the impact on the environment (no pesticides, no artificial fertilisers).

Organic farming methods include:
- using natural fertilisers like animal manure or compost
- growing nitrogen-fixing crops (e.g. peas or clover)
- rotating crops to maintain soil fertility
- avoiding chemical pesticides by weeding
- varying seed planting times to discourage pests.

**Advantages** of organic farming:
- Food crops and the environment aren't contaminated with artificial fertilisers or pesticides.
- Soil erosion is limited, and fertility is maintained through the use of organic fertilisers.
- Biodiversity is promoted because hedgerows and other habitats are conserved.
- Livestock have space to roam.

**Disadvantages** of organic farming:
- It's less efficient because some crops are lost to pests and diseases.
- Organic fertilisers take time to rot and they don't supply a specific balance of minerals.
- It is expensive.
- More space is needed.

## Hydroponics

**Hydroponics** is a way of growing plants without using soil. The plants are grown with their roots in a solution containing the minerals needed for growth. This growing method is useful for **greenhouses** or areas which have very **thin or barren soil**.

Certain plants, e.g. tomatoes, can be grown hydroponically in greenhouses.

(HT) **Advantages** of hydroponics:
- The mineral levels added to the solution can be carefully controlled and adjusted to the type of plant.
- There is a reduced risk of the plants becoming diseased.

**Disadvantages** of hydroponics:
- The plants have to be supported as they have no anchorage for their roots.
- Expensive fertilisers are needed to supply the plant with minerals.

## Biological Control

Some farmers prefer to **introduce a predator**, instead of using a pesticide, to reduce the number of **pests**. This is called **biological control**.

But, it's important to remember that when biological controls or pesticides are used to get rid of pests, the effect on the rest of the organisms in the food chain or web must be considered.

For example, in the food web shown below, if a pest control was to target rabbits, this would have an effect not only on the rabbits, but also on hawks and foxes (who eat rabbits).

**Advantages** of biological control:

- The predator selected only usually attacks the pest (i.e. it's species-specific).
- Once introduced, the predator can have an impact over many years, so repeating treatment isn't required.
- The pest can't become resistant to the predator (unlike pesticides).
- No need for chemical pesticides.

**Disadvantages** of biological control:

- The pest is reduced but it isn't completely removed.
- The predator may not eat the pest or it may even eat useful species.
- The predator may reproduce out of control.
- The predator may leave the area.

**Food Web**

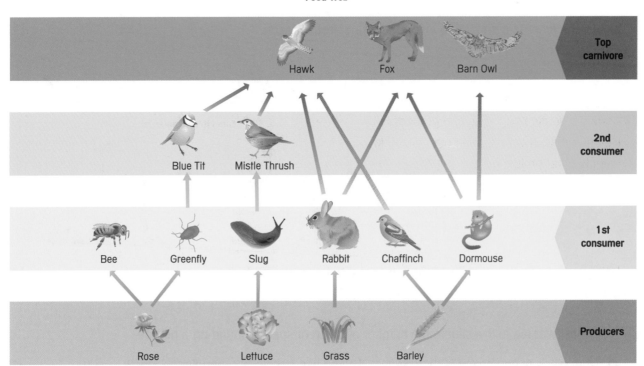

## Quick Test

1. Name four intensive farming techniques.
2. Give two disadvantages of organic farming.
3. HT Give two advantages of hydroponics.

# B4 Exam Practice Questions

1. When Isaac cuts his grass, he puts the grass cuttings in his composter.

   a) Name one type of microorganism that causes the grass cuttings to decay. **[1]**

   _____

   b) Every few weeks, Isaac mixes the compost with a garden fork. Why does he do this and what could happen if he does not? **[4]**

   _____

   _____

   _____

   c) Isaac wants to know the best conditions for decay. Ring the best conditions. **[1]**

   **Warm**　　**Hot**　　**Cold**　　**Dry**　　**Damp**　　**No oxygen**　　**Oxygen**

2. The xylem and phloem help transport in plants.

   a) What is the function of the xylem? **[2]**

   _____

   _____

   b) List the four factors that can affect the rate of transpiration. **[2]**

   1 _____　　2 _____

   3 _____　　4 _____

3. Ahmed investigated the school grounds. He set a pitfall trap and then used a key to identify what he found.

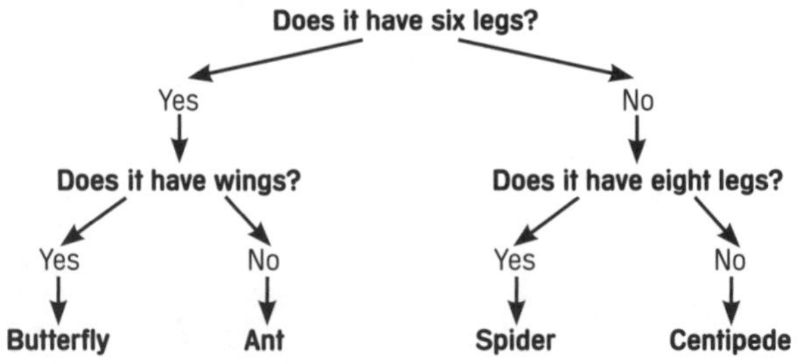

   **Does it have six legs?**

   Yes — **Does it have wings?**　　No — **Does it have eight legs?**

   Yes — **Butterfly**　　No — **Ant**　　Yes — **Spider**　　No — **Centipede**

   Using the information in the key, list two characteristics of a butterfly. **[2]**

   _____

4. A scientist wanted to investigate the number of different species found on a hillside.

   a) What piece of equipment is the scientist likely to use to help her sample the area? **[1]**

   _____

   b) Describe how the scientist could carry out his investigation. **[3]**

   _____

   _____

**c)** A colleague suggests to the scientist that he should have investigated the effect of the slope on the number of species found on the hillside. Suggest a sampling technique that the scientist might use. **[1]**

........................................................................................................................................

**5** Chloe and James monitored the growth of a number of plants around the school grounds.

They put their data into a table.

|  | Plant 1 | Plant 2 | Plant 3 | Plant 4 | Plant 5 |
|---|---|---|---|---|---|
| Location of Plant | Playing fields | Edge of car park | Behind library | Edge of car park | Playing fields |
| Description | Poor growth, yellow leaves | Normal growth, yellow leaves | Normal growth, green leaves | Normal growth, discoloured leaves | Discoloured leaves, underdeveloped flowers |

**a)** What mineral is Plant 1 lacking? ........................................................................... **[1]**

**b)** What mineral is Plant 5 lacking? ........................................................................... **[1]**

**c)** Which location appears to be the best for plants to grow? ................................... **[1]**

**6** Pierre wanted to investigate osmosis. He cut five equal size potato chips, placed them in five different sugar solutions and left them for 24 hours. He measured the mass of the potato chip before and after the investigation. His results are shown in the table.

| Concentration of Sugar Solution (M) | Mass of Potato Chip Before (g) | Mass of Potato Chip After (g) | Difference in Mass (g) |
|---|---|---|---|
| 0 | 1.62 | 1.74 | 0.12 |
| 0.25 | 1.72 | 1.62 | 0.10 |
| 0.5 | 1.69 | 1.62 | 0.07 |
| 0.75 | 1.76 | 1.6 | 0.16 |
| 1 | 1.74 | 1.5 | 0.24 |

**a)** In which concentration did the potato gain mass? ................................................. **[1]**

**b)** What caused this gain in mass? **[1]**

........................................................................................................................................

**c)** Suggest how Pierre could increase the reliability of his results. **[1]**

........................................................................................................................................

**7** Look at this diagram of a palisade cell in a plant.

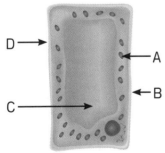

**a)** One letter shows the vacuole. Which letter is it? Tick (✓) the correct answer. **[1]**

A ◯   B ◯   C ◯   D ◯

**HT b)** Explain why the upper epidermis in a leaf is transparent. **[1]**

........................................................................................................................................

# Fundamental Chemical Concepts

You need to have a good understanding of the concepts (ideas) on these four pages, so make sure you revise this section before each exam.

## Atoms

All substances are made up of **atoms**. Atoms have:

- a **positively** charged **nucleus** made of **protons** and **neutrons** (except hydrogen)
- **negatively** charged **electrons** that orbit the nucleus.

| Atomic Particle | Relative Charge |
|---|---|
| Proton | +1 |
| Neutron | 0 |
| Electron | -1 |

An atom contains the same number of electrons (negatively charged particles) and protons (positively charged particles), so each atom is electrically neutral. This means that it has no overall charge.

**A Fluorine Atom**

Key: ● Proton ● Neutron ✖ Electron

## Elements and Compounds

An **element** is a substance made up of just one type of atom. Each element is represented by a different chemical symbol, for example:

- Fe represents iron
- Na represents sodium.

These symbols are all arranged in the **periodic table**.

**Compounds** are substances formed from the atoms of more than one element, which have been joined together by a chemical bond:

- **Covalent** bonds – two atoms **share** a pair of **electrons**. (The atoms in molecules are held together by covalent bonds.)
- **Ionic** bonds – atoms **lose electrons** to become **positive ions** or **gain electrons** to become **negative ions**. The attraction between oppositely charged ions is an **ionic bond**.

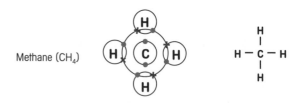

**A Covalent Bond between Hydrogen and Carbon in Methane**

Methane ($CH_4$)

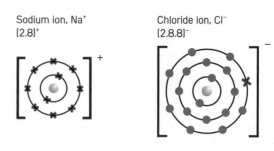

**An Ionic Bond between Sodium and Chlorine in Sodium Chloride**

Sodium ion, $Na^+$
$[2.8]^+$

Chloride ion, $Cl^-$
$[2.8.8]^-$

# Fundamental Chemical Concepts

## Formulae

**Chemical symbols** are used with numbers to write **formulae** that represent compounds. Formulae are used to show:

- the different elements in a compound
- the number of atoms of each element in the formula.

If there are brackets around part of the formula, everything inside the brackets is multiplied by the number outside.

**Calcium Nitrate**

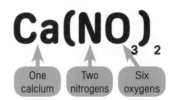

$(NO_3)_2$ means $2 \times NO_3$, i.e. $NO_3 + NO_3$.

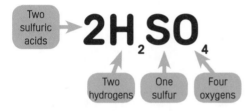

Sulfuric Acid

## Displayed Formulae

A **displayed formula** shows you the arrangement of atoms in a compound.

A displayed formula shows:

- the different types of atom in the molecule, (e.g. carbon, hydrogen)
- the number of each different type of atom
- the bonds between the atoms.

Ethanol, $C_2H_5OH$     Ethene, $C_2H_4$

## Equations

In a chemical reaction the substances that you start with are called **reactants**. During the reaction, the atoms in the reactants are rearranged to form new substances called **products**.

We use equations to show what has happened during a chemical reaction. The reactants are on the left of the equation and the products are on the right.

No atoms are lost or gained during a chemical reaction so the equation must be balanced: there must always be the same number and type of atoms on both sides of the equation.

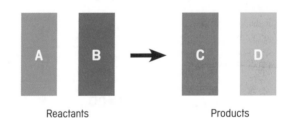

Reactants       Products

# Fundamental Chemical Concepts

## Writing Balanced Equations

### Example 1

1 Write a word equation.

2 Substitute in symbols and formulae.

3 Balance the equation.
- First, you need to add another MgO to the product side to balance the Os.
- You now need to add another Mg on the reactant side to balance the Mgs.
- There are two magnesium atoms and two oxygen atoms on each side – it's balanced.

4 Write a balanced symbol equation.

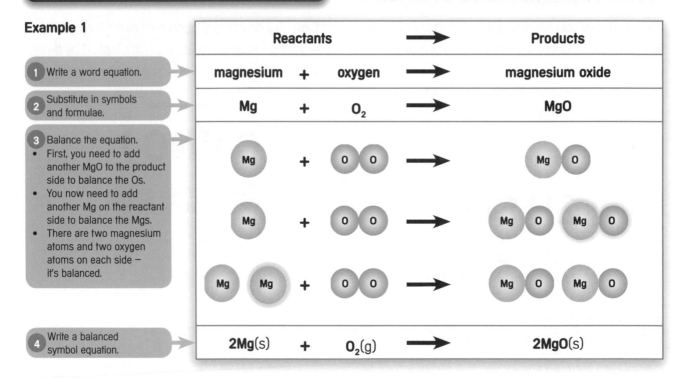

When you write equations, you may be asked to include the **state symbols**: (aq) for aqueous solutions (dissolved in water), (g) for gases, (l) for liquids and (s) for solids.

HT You should be able to balance equations by looking at the formulae (i.e. without drawing the atoms).

1 Write a word equation.

2 Substitute in symbols and formulae.

3 Balance the equation.

4 Write a balanced symbol equation with state symbols.

Equations can also be written using displayed formulae. These must be balanced too.

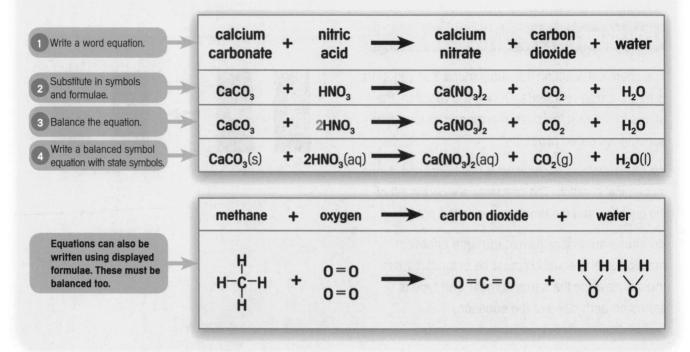

# Fundamental Chemical Concepts

## Compounds and their Formulae

### Acids

| Ethanoic acid | $CH_3COOH$ |
|---|---|
| Hydrochloric acid | HCl |
| (HT) Nitric acid | $HNO_3$ |
| (HT) Sulfuric acid | $H_2SO_4$ |

### Carbonates

| Calcium carbonate | $CaCO_3$ |
|---|---|
| Copper(II) carbonate | $CuCO_3$ |
| (HT) Magnesium carbonate | $MgCO_3$ |
| (HT) Sodium carbonate | $Na_2CO_3$ |
| (HT) Zinc carbonate | $ZnCO_3$ |

### Chlorides

| Ammonium chloride | $NH_4Cl$ |
|---|---|
| (HT) Calcium chloride | $CaCl_2$ |
| (HT) Magnesium chloride | $MgCl_2$ |
| Potassium chloride | KCl |
| Silver chloride | AgCl |
| Sodium chloride | NaCl |

### Oxides

| Aluminium oxide | $Al_2O_3$ |
|---|---|
| Copper(II) oxide | CuO |
| Iron(II) oxide | FeO |
| (HT) Magnesium oxide | MgO |
| (HT) Manganese oxide | $MnO_2$ |
| (HT) Sulfur dioxide | $SO_2$ |
| (HT) Zinc oxide | ZnO |

### Hydroxides

| Copper(II) hydroxide | $Cu(OH)_2$ |
|---|---|
| Iron(II) hydroxide | $Fe(OH)_2$ |
| (HT) Potassium hydroxide | KOH |
| (HT) Sodium hydroxide | NaOH |

### Sulfates

| (HT) Ammonium sulfate | $(NH_4)_2SO_4$ |
|---|---|
| (HT) Magnesium sulfate | $MgSO_4$ |
| (HT) Potassium sulfate | $K_2SO_4$ |
| (HT) Sodium sulfate | $Na_2SO_4$ |
| (HT) Zinc sulfate | $ZnSO_4$ |

### Others

| Ammonia | $NH_3$ |
|---|---|
| Calcium hydrogencarbonate | $Ca(HCO_3)_2$ |
| Carbon dioxide | $CO_2$ |
| Carbon monoxide | CO |
| Chlorine | $Cl_2$ |
| Ethane | $C_2H_6$ |
| (HT) Ethanol | $C_2H_5OH$ |
| (HT) Glucose | $C_6H_{12}O_6$ |
| Hydrogen | $H_2$ |
| Methane | $CH_4$ |
| Oxygen | $O_2$ |
| (HT) Silver nitrate | $AgNO_3$ |
| Water | $H_2O$ |

## Quick Test

1. What are the negative particles in an atom called?
2. Where are the protons and neutrons found in an atom?
3. What is an ion?
4. What three things can displayed formulae tell you?

# C3 Rate of Reaction (1)

## Collision Theory

Reactions happen at different speeds, for example:
- rusting is a slow reaction
- burning and an explosion are fast reactions.

The rate of reaction measures the amount of product made in a specific time.

The rate of reaction can be measured in:
- g/s or g/min for mass changes
- $cm^3$/s or $cm^3$/min for volume changes.

The rate of a reaction can be increased by:
- raising the temperature
- increasing the concentration (of liquids)
- increasing the pressure (of gases).

## Rate of Reaction Experiments

Chemical reactions **stop** when one of the **reactants** is **used up**. The amount of **product formed** depends on the amount of reactant **used**.

Often there is not the same amount of each type of reactant. The limiting reactant is the one that is used up by the end of the reaction.

(HT) If there are more reactants, there are more reactant particles so more product particles can be made. The limiting reactant determines the maximum amount of product that can be made.

You can measure the rate of a reaction by monitoring the mass of a reaction mixture in a flask on a top pan balance or measuring the volume of a gas produced using a gas syringe.

## Analysing the Rate of Reactions

From a graph, you can find out the following:

1. How long it takes to make the maximum amount of products by drawing a vertical line down to the *x*-axis (time) from the flat line. (The flat line on the graph shows that the reaction is finished.)
2. How much product was made by drawing a horizontal line from the highest point on the graph across to the *y*-axis.
3. Which reaction is quicker by comparing the steepness of the lines.

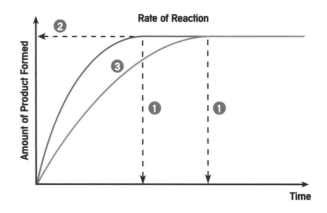

(HT) The **rate of reaction** can be calculated from the **slope** of a **graph** (gradient). From this you can **extrapolate** (calculate further data) and **interpolate** (create missing data). For example, you can:

1. Calculate the initial rate of reaction by drawing a straight line following the start of the curve. Now calculate the gradient and this is the rate of reaction.
2. Work out the amount of product formed for a time for which you don't have a reading.
3. Extend the curve to estimate its likely path.

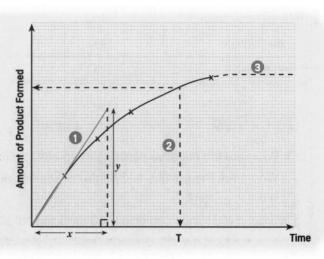

**Key Words**                 **Reactant • Product**

## Temperature of the Reactants

**Chemical reactions** happen when **particles collide** with **enough energy**. The **more** collisions there are between particles, the **faster** the **reaction**.

In a reaction at **low temperature**, the particles move slowly. This means that the particles collide less often, and at lower energy, so fewer collisions will be successful. The rate of reaction will be slow.

In a reaction at **high temperature**, the particles move fast. This means that particles collide more often, and at higher energy. The rate of reaction will be fast.

Low Temperature

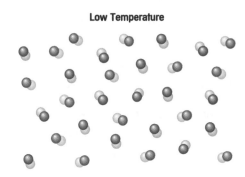

High Temperature

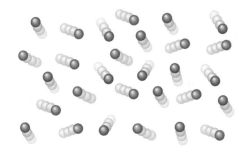

## ⒽⓉ Increasing Temperature

Increasing temperature causes an increase in the **kinetic energy** of the particles, i.e. they move a lot faster.

The faster the particles move, the greater the chance of them colliding, so the number of collisions per second increases:

- More frequent collisions between particles lead to a faster reaction.

When the particles collide at an increased temperature they have more energy. High energy collisions increase the chance of it being a successful collision:

- More energetic collisions lead to more successful collisions.

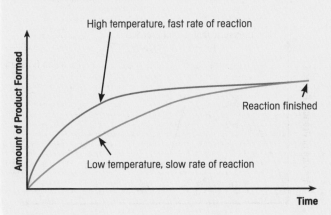

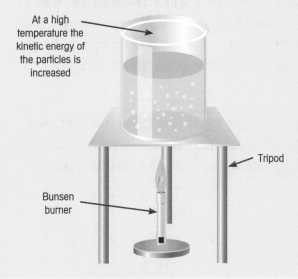

At a high temperature the kinetic energy of the particles is increased

Tripod

Bunsen burner

# C3 Rate of Reaction (2)

## Concentration of the Reactants

In a reaction where one or both reactants are in **low concentrations**, the particles will be spread out. The particles will collide with each other less often, so there will be fewer successful collisions.

If there is a **high concentration** of one or both reactants, the particles will be crowded close together. The particles will collide with each other more often, so there will be many more successful collisions.

(HT) Increasing concentration increases the number of particles in the same space, i.e. the particles are much more crowded together.

The more crowded the particles are, the greater the chance of them colliding, which increases the number of collisions per second:
- More frequent collisions lead to a faster reaction.

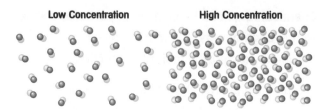

Low Concentration    High Concentration

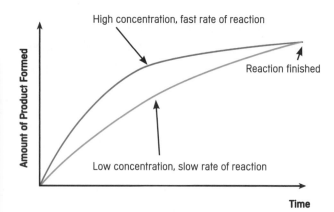

High concentration, fast rate of reaction

Reaction finished

Low concentration, slow rate of reaction

Amount of Product Formed

Time

## Pressure of a Gas

When a gas is under a **low pressure**, the particles are spread out. The particles will collide with each other less often so there will be fewer successful collisions. (This is like low concentration of reactants in solution.)

When the **pressure is high**, the particles are crowded more closely together. The particles collide more often, resulting in many more successful collisions. (This is like high concentration of reactants in solution.)

(HT) You may be asked to extrapolate or interpolate data on a graph. You may also be asked to calculate the gradient to give a value for the rate of reaction.

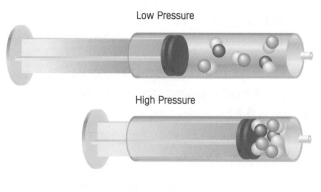

Low Pressure

High Pressure

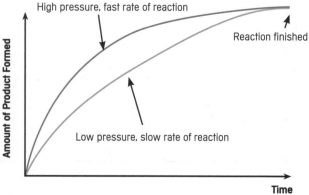

High pressure, fast rate of reaction

Reaction finished

Low pressure, slow rate of reaction

Amount of Product Formed

Time

## Surface Area of Solid Reactants

The **larger** the **surface area** of a reactant, the **faster** the reaction. **Powdered solids** have a larger surface area compared to their volume than **lumps of solid**. This means there are **more particles** on the **surface** for the other reactants to collide with.

The greater the number of particles exposed, the greater the chance of them colliding, which **increases** the rate of the **reaction**. So, powders can have very fast reactions, much faster than a lump of the same reactant.

**HT** A greater proportion of particles exposed in a powdered solid means the particles have a **greater chance** of **colliding**, which means the frequency of collisions increases. (There are more collisions each second.)

An explosion is a very fast reaction where huge volumes of gas are made.

Workers in factories that handle powders, such as flour, custard powder or sulfur, have to be very careful because the **dust** of these materials can **mix** with **air** and could cause an **explosion** if there is a **spark**.

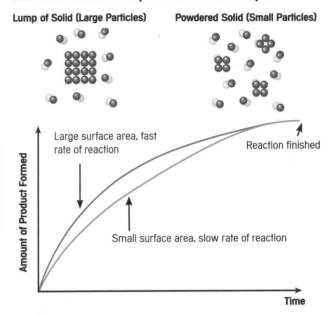

## Using a Catalyst

A **catalyst** is a substance that **changes** the rate of a chemical **reaction** without being used up or changed at the end of the reaction. Catalysts are often used to speed up the rate of reaction.

Catalysts are very useful materials, as only a **small amount** of catalyst is needed to speed up the reaction of large amounts of reactant.

You can see how a catalyst affects the rate of reaction by looking at a graph. This graph shows two reactions that eventually produce the same amount of product. One reaction takes place much faster than the other because a catalyst is used.

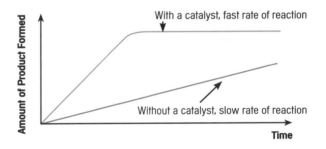

**HT** You may be asked to extrapolate or interpolate data on a graph. You may also be asked to calculate the gradient to give a value for the rate of reaction.

## Quick Test

1. What is rate of reaction?
2. Give an example of units which could be used to measure the rate of reaction for mass change reactions.
3. How can rate of reaction be increased?
4. Explain how temperature can increase the rate of reaction.

# C3 Reacting Masses

## Relative Atomic Mass, $A_r$

Every element has its own **relative atomic mass**, $A_r$.

Each element in the periodic table has two numbers. The **larger** of the two numbers is the $A_r$, for example the $A_r$ of carbon is 12.

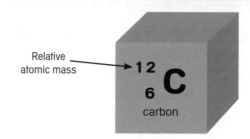

Relative atomic mass → $^{12}_{6}$ C carbon

## Relative Formula Mass, $M_r$

The **relative formula mass**, $M_r$, of a compound is the sum of the relative atomic masses of all the atoms present in the formula.

Follow these steps to calculate the $M_r$:

1. Write down the formula of the compound.
2. Multiply the number of atoms of each element in the formula by its $A_r$.
3. Add them all up.

### Example 1

Calculate the relative formula mass of $H_2SO_4$.

Write the symbols | Multiply the number of atoms in the formula by the $A_r$

| | | |
|---|---|---|
| H | 2 × 1 | = 2 |
| S | 1 × 32 | = 32 |
| O | 4 × 16 | = 64 |
| | $M_r$ = | **98** |

Add them all up

### Example 2

Calculate the relative formula mass of $Ca(OH)_2$

| | | |
|---|---|---|
| Ca | 1 × 40 | = 40 |
| O | 2 × 16 | = 32 |
| H | 2 × 1 | = 2 |
| | $M_r$ = | **74** |

## Calculating Reactants and Products

To calculate how much substance a reaction will produce (**product**), or the amount of starting materials (**reactant**) you need, you must remember the following:

- The total mass of the reactants always equals the total mass of the products as no atoms are created or destroyed in a chemical reaction.
- The more reactants you start with, the greater the amount of product formed.

Substances react in simple **ratios**. You can use the ratio to calculate how much of each reactant is needed to produce a certain amount of product.

The mass of the product is directly proportional to the mass of the reactant.

Sometimes you know the starting mass of only one reactant and the final mass of the product. You can use this method to work out the missing mass.

### Example 1

4.8g of magnesium reacts with oxygen to make 8.0g of magnesium oxide. What mass of oxygen will be used?

| | | | | |
|---|---|---|---|---|
| magnesium | **+** | oxygen | → | magnesium oxide |
| 4.8g | **+** | oxygen | → | 8.0g |

Mass of oxygen = 8.0 − 4.8 = 3.2g

 HT

| | | | | |
|---|---|---|---|---|
| **2Mg** | **+** | **O₂** | → | **2MgO** |
| 2 × 24 = 48g | | 2 × 16 = 32g | | 2 × (24 + 16) = 80g |

If 48g of magnesium needs 32g of oxygen but we have only 4.8g then we need 3.2g of oxygen.

## Calculating Reactants and Products (Cont.)

### Example 2

Calcium carbonate decomposes to make calcium oxide and carbon dioxide in the mass ratio 100 : 56 : 44. The ratio is made of the $M_r$ for each reactant or product.

| Calcium carbonate | → | Calcium oxide | + | Carbon dioxide |
|---|---|---|---|---|
| 100g | → | 56g | + | 44g |

**a)** Calculate how much of the reactant you would need to make 56kg of calcium oxide.

> 1kg = 1000g, so multiply all the quantities by 1000 to get the amounts in kg.

| Calcium carbonate | → | Calcium oxide | + | Carbon dioxide |
|---|---|---|---|---|
| 100kg | → | **56kg** | + | 44kg |

**b)** Calculate how much calcium carbonate you would need to make 4g of carbon dioxide.

> $4g = \frac{44g}{11}$ so divide all the quantities by 11

| Calcium carbonate | → | Calcium oxide | + | Carbon dioxide |
|---|---|---|---|---|
| $\frac{100g}{11} = 9.09g$ | → | $\frac{56g}{11} = 5.1g$ | + | $\frac{44g}{11} = 4g$ |

## (HT) Calculating Masses

The **total mass** of **reactants equals** the **total mass** of **products** because **no atoms** are **gained** or **lost** in a chemical reaction. There is exactly the same number of atoms; they are just rearranged into different substances.

To work out how much of a substance is used up or produced use this method:

1. Write down the balanced symbol equation for the reaction.
2. Work out the $M_r$ of each substance.
3. Check that the total mass of reactants equals the total mass of the products.
4. Ignore the substances not mentioned in the question, and create a ratio of mass of reactant to mass of product for the substances that are mentioned.
5. Use the ratio to calculate how much of the named substance can be produced or is needed for the reaction.

### Example

1. $HNO_3$ + $NH_3$ → $NH_4NO_3$
2. $1 + 14 + (3 \times 16)$ + $14 + (3 \times 1)$ → $14 + (1 \times 4) + 14 + (3 \times 16)$
3. $63$ + $17$ → $80$
4. $63$ : $17$ : $80$
5. If 63kg of nitric acid and 17kg of ammonia produces 80kg of ammonium nitrate then 1kg of nitric acid and 0.3kg of ammonia would produce:

$\frac{80}{63} = $ **1.3kg of ammonium nitrate**

# C3 Percentage Yield and Atom Economy

## Percentage Yield

**Percentage yield** is a way of comparing the amount of product made (**actual yield**) to the amount of product expected to be made (**predicted yield**).

You can calculate percentage yield by using this formula:

$$\text{Percentage yield} = \frac{\text{Actual yield}}{\text{Predicted yield}} \times 100$$

- A 100% yield means that no product has been lost (actual yield is the same as predicted yield).
- A 0% yield means that no product has been made (actual yield is zero).

### Example

A reaction was expected to produce a mass of 10g. But, the actual mass produced was 8g. Calculate the percentage yield.

$$\text{Percentage yield} = \frac{\text{Actual yield}}{\text{Predicted yield}} \times 100$$
$$= \frac{8g}{10g} \times 100 = \textbf{80\%}$$

There are several reasons why the percentage yield is less than the expected yield. The products could be lost in **evaporation**, **filtration** or during the **transfer of liquids**. Also not all reactants may have been used to make the products.

**HT** In industrial processes a high percentage yield is desired. This reduces waste and therefore cost.

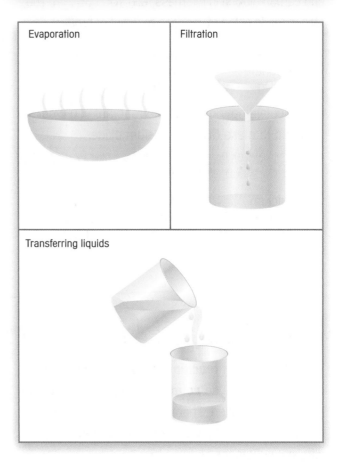

Evaporation | Filtration | Transferring liquids

## Atom Economy

**Atom economy** is a way of measuring the number of atoms that are wasted in a chemical reaction. If all the atoms in the reactants are in the product, then the atom economy is 100%.

### Example

In the hydration of ethene to make ethanol:

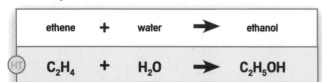

| ethene | + | water | → | ethanol |
|--------|---|-------|---|---------|

**HT** $C_2H_4$ + $H_2O$ → $C_2H_5OH$

Atom economy can be calculated by using the following equation:

$$\text{Atom economy} = \frac{M_r \text{ of desired products} \times 100}{\text{Sum of } M_r \text{ of all the products}}$$

All of the atoms in the reactants are used in the product.

So, atom economy $= \dfrac{46 \times 100}{46} = 100\%$

The higher the atom economy, the 'greener' the chemical reaction.

**HT** In an industrial process a high atom economy is wanted as this reduces the amount of unwanted products and makes the process more sustainable.

In your exam you may be asked to look at a balanced symbol equation and say why a process has 100% atom economy or less than 100% atom economy.

## Exothermic and Endothermic Reactions

**Chemical reactions** either **give out** or **take in** energy. So chemical reactions cause a temperature change.

**Exothermic** reactions release energy to the surroundings and cause a temperature rise.

**Endothermic** reactions absorb energy from the surroundings and cause a temperature drop.

The energy given out by exothermic chemical reactions can be used to:

- heat things
- produce electricity
- make sound
- make light.

Energy is measured in **joules (J)** or **kilojoules (kJ)**.

Temperature is measured in **degrees Celsius (°C)**.

## Comparing Fuels

A **calorimeter** can be used to compare the amounts of heat energy released by the combustion of different fuels. This is a **calorimetry** experiment.

If you burn the same mass of each fuel, the fuel that produces the largest temperature rise releases the most energy.

The formula used to work out the change in temperature (°C) is:

$$\text{Temperature change} = \text{Final temperature of water (°C)} - \text{Start temperature of water (°C)}$$

To make meaningful comparisons (i.e. to do a **fair test**) you need to:

- use the same mass (or volume) of water
- use the same calorimeter
- have the burner and calorimeter the same distance apart
- burn the same mass of fuel.

To make your calorimetry reliable you should repeat your experiment and take an average (mean) of the temperature rise. To help you compare between fuels, you may wish to calculate the energy released per gram of fuel. To do this you would need to measure the mass of the spirit burner before and after the experiment.

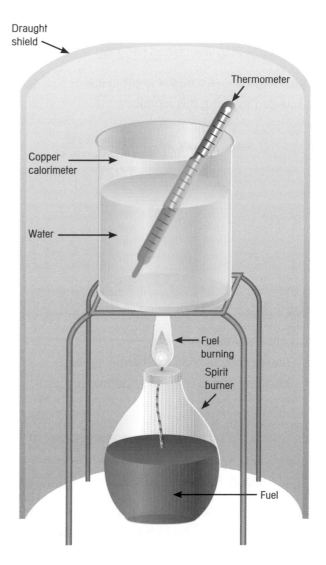

**A Calorimetry Experiment**

Draught shield

Thermometer

Copper calorimeter

Water

Fuel burning

Spirit burner

Fuel

# C3 Energy

## Calculating Energy Changes

To compare fuels, you need to work out the amount of energy transferred by the fuel to the water in the **calorimetry** experiment. The amount of energy transferred can be calculated by using the following formula:

| Energy transferred (J) | = | Mass of water heated (g) | × | Specific heat capacity (J/g/°C) | × | Change in temperature (°C) |
|---|---|---|---|---|---|---|
| q | = | M | × | C | × | $\Delta T$ |

*N.B. Specific heat capacity is a constant that is specific to a particular material. Water has a value of 4.2J/g/°C.*

(HT) To compare fuels you need to work out the amount of energy transferred per gram of fuel burned.

The energy transferred per gram of fuel is calculated by using this formula:

$$\text{Energy per gram} = \frac{\text{Energy supplied (J)}}{\text{Mass of fuel burned (g)}}$$

### Example

The results from a calorimeter experiment with hexane are as follows:

- Mass of hexane burned = 0.26g
- Rise in temperature of water = 12°C
- Mass of water in calorimeter = 200g

Calculate the energy transferred.

| Energy transferred (J) | = | Mass of water heated (g) | × | Specific heat capacity (J/g/°C) | × | Change in temperature (°C) |
|---|---|---|---|---|---|---|

Energy transferred = 200g × 4.2J/g/°C × 12°C

**= 10 080 joules**

### Example

Calculate the amount of energy per gram of hexane fuel.

$$\text{Energy per gram} = \frac{\text{Energy supplied (J)}}{\text{Mass of fuel burned (g)}}$$

$$\text{Energy per gram} = \frac{10\,080J}{0.26g}$$

**= 38 769J/g**

*N.B. The actual value for hexane is 48 407J/g. Our result is lower because some energy is lost to the surroundings and some is transferred to the calorimeter.*

## Making and Breaking Bonds

In a chemical reaction:
- **making** bonds is an **exothermic** process
- **breaking** bonds is an **endothermic** process.

(HT) Chemical reactions that need more energy to break bonds than released when new bonds are made are **endothermic reactions.**

Chemical reactions that release more energy when making bonds than breaking them are **exothermic reactions**.

### Quick Test

1. When 12g of carbon is completely burned in oxygen, 10g of carbon dioxide is made. Calculate the percentage yield.
2. What is the formula for atom economy?
3. In the blue Bunsen flame, methane burns with lots of oxygen to make carbon dioxide and water only.
   a) Write a word equation for this reaction.
   b) Is this reaction exothermic or endothermic?

## Batch and Continuous Processes

In a **batch process**, reactants are put into a reactor and the product is removed at the end of the reaction. Medicines and pharmaceutical drugs can be made in this way. Batch processes:

- make a product on demand and on a small scale
- can be used to make a variety of products
- are labour intensive – the reactor needs to be filled, emptied and cleaned.

In a **continuous process,** reactants are continually fed into the reactor as the products are removed. The production of ammonia in the Haber process and sulfuric acid in the Contact process are made in this way. Continuous processes:

- make a product on a large scale
- are dedicated to making just one product
- operate all the time
- can run automatically.

## Making and Developing Medicines

The materials used to make a medicine can be extracted from plant materials by:

- **crushing** – using a pestle and mortar
- **boiling and dissolving** – using a suitable solvent
- **chromatography** – using chromatography to separate a concentrated solution.

Developing a new pharmaceutical drug is very expensive and takes a long time. The drug must also be approved for use, and satisfy all the legal requirements set out by the government.

The costs include:

- **materials** needed – they could be synthetic or natural
- **research** development and **testing** which can take many years
- **labour** – highly qualified staff are needed and often lots of staff are needed. It can't be automated (carried out by machines) as only small quantities are made
- **energy**
- **marketing**.

It is important that pharmaceutical drugs are as pure as possible. **Thin layer chromatography** (TLC) can be used to test the purity of a chemical. Testing the melting and boiling point can help to identify the compound and infer its purity.

(HT) Research and development can take a few years, but it can take even longer to carry out **safety tests**, including testing on human volunteers. There are very strict legal rules which a new medicine must satisfy before it can be put on the market.

A pharmaceutical company may invest hundreds of millions of pounds to develop one drug. But they have a limited time to recoup their investment before they lose exclusive rights to make the medicine. If the number of people using the medicine is small, then the cost of buying the drug would be very high.

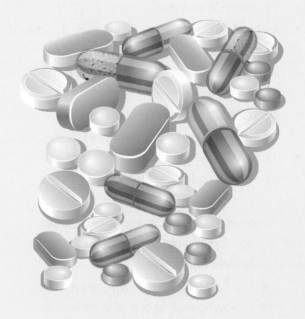

# C3 Allotropes of Carbon and Nanochemistry

## Carbon

There are three forms of carbon you need to know:

- **diamond**
- **graphite**
- **buckminster fullerene** (buckyballs).

These are all **allotropes** of carbon. Allotropes are different forms of the same element with atoms arranged in different structures.

All of these substances are made only of carbon atoms and have different structures.

## Diamond

**Diamond** has a rigid structure:

- It's insoluble in water and doesn't conduct electricity.
- It's used in jewellery because it's colourless, clear (transparent) and lustrous (shiny).
- It can be used in cutting tools because it's very hard and has a very high melting point.
- It is a giant molecular structure.

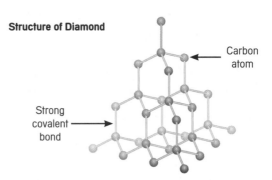

**Structure of Diamond**

Carbon atom

Strong covalent bond

(HT) **Diamond** is made of carbon atoms bonded to four other carbon atoms by strong **covalent bonds**.

- It doesn't have any free electrons so it doesn't conduct electricity.

- It's hard and has a high melting point because of the large number of covalent bonds These bonds need a lot of energy to break.

## Graphite

**Graphite** has a layered structure:

- It's insoluble in water.
- It's black and slippery, which is why it's used in pencil leads.
- It's lustrous and opaque (light can't travel through it).
- It conducts electricity and has a very high melting point, so is used to make electrodes for electrolysis.
- It's slippery, so it's used in lubricants.
- It is a giant molecular structure.

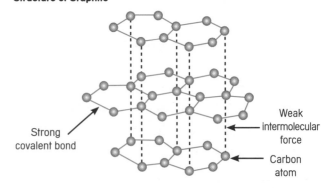

**Structure of Graphite**

Strong covalent bond

Weak intermolecular force

Carbon atom

(HT) **Graphite** is made of layers of carbon atoms that are bonded to three other carbon atoms by strong **covalent bonds**.

- The layers are held together by weak intermolecular forces, allowing each layer to slide easily.

- It conducts electricity because it has **free** (delocalised) **electrons**.
- It has a high melting point because it has many strong covalent bonds to break. These bonds need a lot of energy to break.

## Buckminster Fullerene

A **Buckminster Fullerene** molecule ($C_{60}$) – known as a 'buckyball' – is made of 60 carbon atoms arranged in a football-like sphere. It is a black solid.

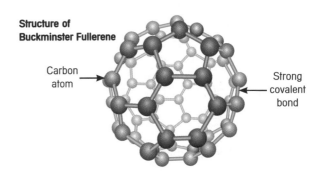

Structure of Buckminster Fullerene

Carbon atom

Strong covalent bond

## Nanochemistry and Nanotubes

**Chemistry** deals with materials on a **large scale**, but nanochemistry deals with materials on an **atomic scale** (i.e. individual atoms).

Chemists discovered that **nanotubes** could be made by joining fullerenes together. Nanotubes conduct electricity and are very strong. They are used to:

- reinforce graphite tennis racquets because of their strength
- make connectors and semiconductors in circuits because of their electrical properties
- develop more efficient industrial catalysts.

Fullerenes and nanotubes can be used to 'cage' other molecules because their shape allows them to trap other substances, for example:

- **drugs**, e.g. a major new HIV treatment uses buckyballs to deliver a material which disrupts the working of the HIV virus

(HT) • **catalysts** – by attaching catalyst material to a nanotube, a massive surface area can be achieved, making the catalyst very efficient.

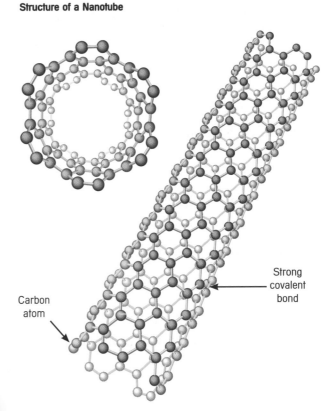

Structure of a Nanotube

Carbon atom

Strong covalent bond

## Quick Test

1. Give an example of a chemical that is made by batch production.
2. What are the four stages for extracting chemicals from plants?
3. Name three allotropes of carbon.
4. What is the formula of buckminster fullerene?

# C3 Exam Practice Questions

**1** **a)** Using the periodic table to help you, calculate the relative formula mass of each of the following compounds.

    **i)** $Na_2CO_3$ **[2]**

    **ii)** $(NH_4)_2SO_4$ **[3]**

**b)** A neutralisation reaction was expected to produce a salt with a mass of 15g. The actual mass was 9g.

Calculate the percentage yield. **[2]**

**2** **a)** Pharmaceutical drugs are made using a batch process.

Explain why the materials needed to make new medicines are expensive. **[1]**

**b)** Describe the advantages of using a batch process to make a chemical. **[3]**

**3** Collision theory can be used to explain how changing conditions affects the rate of reaction.

**a)** What must happen to particles in order for a reaction to take place? **[2]**

**b)** What happens to particles when you increase the concentration? **[2]**

**c)** How does increasing the temperature increase the rate of reaction? **[2]**

**4** When powdered calcium carbonate is put into an acid it reacts quicker than if a lump of calcium carbonate was used.

Explain why the powdered solid reacts faster than a lump of the same substance. **[3]**

**5** When magnesium metal is put into a beaker of hydrochloric acid a chemical reaction happens. Chantal completed an experiment to measure the gas made in the reaction. She plotted her results on the graph to the right.

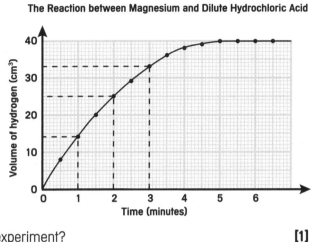

The Reaction between Magnesium and Dilute Hydrochloric Acid

a) What was the independent variable in Chantal's experiment? **[1]**

b) What was the maximum volume of gas made in this experiment? **[1]**

c) When did the reaction stop? **[1]**

**6** Rate of reaction can be measured by monitoring the amount of product made over time. This data can then be put on a graph.

a) Write down two factors that affect the rate of reaction. **[2]**

HT

b) How can you use a graph to calculate the rate of reaction? **[1]**

**7** Iron combusts in oxygen to make iron oxide ($Fe_2O_3$).

a) Write a balanced symbol equation for this reaction. **[3]**

b) Calculate the relative formula mass ($M_r$) for iron oxide. ($A_r$ of Fe = 56, $A_r$ of O = 16) **[2]**

c) Mass is conserved in this chemical reaction. Use relative formula mass and atomic masses to show this. **[4]**

# C4 Atomic Structure

## History of the Atom

The model of atomic structure has changed over time as new evidence has been found. In the early 1800s **John Dalton** proposed the theory that all atoms of the same element were the same. In the late 1890s **J. J. Thomson** discovered the electron. In 1911 **Ernest Rutherford** discovered that the atom had a dense centre called the nucleus. Then in 1913 Niels Bohr predicted that electrons occupy orbitals.

It is the work of all these scientists that have led to the current theory of atomic structure.

(HT) Some unexpected results from scientists like Geiger and Marsden have led to the model of the atom being modified in order to explain them.

## Structure of an Atom

An **atom** has a central **nucleus** surrounded by shells of negatively charged **electrons**.

The nucleus is made up of **protons** and **neutrons**. The nucleus is positively charged but the atom has no overall charge.

| Atomic Particle | Relative Charge | Relative Mass |
|---|---|---|
| Proton | +1 | 1 |
| Neutron | 0 | 1 |
| Electron | −1 | 0.0005 (zero) |

(HT) An atom has no overall charge because it has the **same number** of (positive) **protons** and (negative) **electrons**. So, the charges **cancel** each other out.

Atoms have a radius of about $1^{-10}$m and a mass of about $10^{-23}$g.

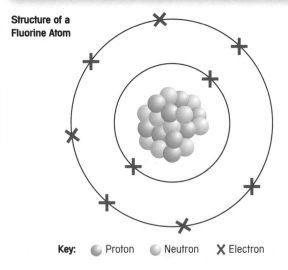

Structure of a
Fluorine Atom

Key: ● Proton ● Neutron ✗ Electron

## Elements and Compounds

An **element** is made of one type of atom. Elements can't be chemically broken down. There are just over 100 naturally occurring elements.

A **compound** is a substance made of two or more elements that are **chemically combined**. You can identify the elements in a compound from its formula, using the periodic table.

For example:
- the **compound** sodium chloride (NaCl) contains the **elements** sodium (Na) and chlorine (Cl)
- the **compound** potassium nitrate ($KNO_3$) contains the **elements** potassium (K), nitrogen (N) and oxygen (O).

**Key Words** | Atom • Nucleus • Electron • Proton • Neutron • Element • Compound

## Mass Number and Atomic Number

The **mass number** is the total number of **protons** and **neutrons** in an atom.

The **atomic number** (proton number) is the number of **protons** in an atom.

The elements in the periodic table are arranged in **increasing atomic number**.

You can use the periodic table to find:
- an element from its atomic number
- the atomic number of an element.

The group number is the same as the number of electrons in the outer shell of an element's atom. The period number is the same as the number of occupied shells (i.e. shells that contain electrons) that an element's atom has.

You can work out the number of protons, electrons and neutrons in an atom or ion if you know its atomic number, mass number and charge.

| Element Symbol | Protons | Electrons | Neutrons |
|---|---|---|---|
| Hydrogen atom $^{1}_{1}H$ | 1 | 1 | 0 <br> $1 - 1 = 0$ |
| Helium atom $^{4}_{2}He$ | 2 | 2 | 2 <br> $4 - 2 = 2$ |
| Sodium atom $^{23}_{11}Na$ | 11 | 11 | 12 <br> $23 - 11 = 12$ |
| Oxide ion $^{16}_{8}O^{2-}$ | 8 | $8 + 2 = 10$ | 8 <br> $16 - 8 = 8$ |

## Isotopes

**Isotopes** are **atoms** of the **same element** that have the **same atomic number** but a **different mass number**.

For example, chlorine has two isotopes:

| $^{35}_{17}Cl$ | Mass number = 35 <br> Atomic number = 17 |
|---|---|

| $^{37}_{17}Cl$ | Mass number = 37 <br> Atomic number = 17 |
|---|---|

(HT) You can identify isotopes from data about the number of electrons, protons and neutrons in particles. Each isotope has the **same number of** **protons** and **electrons**, but a **different number** of **neutrons**. For example, carbon has three main isotopes, as listed in this table:

| Isotope | Symbol | Mass Number | Atomic Number | Protons | Neutrons | Electrons |
|---|---|---|---|---|---|---|
| Carbon-12 | $^{12}_{6}C$ | 12 | 6 | 6 | 6 | 6 |
| Carbon-13 | $^{13}_{6}C$ | 13 | 6 | 6 | 7 | 6 |
| Carbon-14 | $^{14}_{6}C$ | 14 | 6 | 6 | 8 | 6 |

## HT Electron Configuration

Electron configuration tells you how the electrons are arranged around the nucleus in **shells (energy levels)**:

The first shell can hold a maximum of two electrons, and the second shell and the outer shell have a maximum of eight electrons.

| Hydrogen, H<br>Atomic No. = 1 | Helium, He<br>Atomic No. = 2 | Lithium, Li<br>Atomic No. = 3 | Beryllium, Be<br>Atomic No. = 4 |
|---|---|---|---|
| 1 | 2 | 2.1 | 2.2 |
| Boron, B<br>Atomic No. = 5 | Carbon, C<br>Atomic No. = 6 | Nitrogen, N<br>Atomic No. = 7 | Oxygen, O<br>Atomic No. = 8 |
| 2.3 | 2.4 | 2.5 | 2.6 |
| Fluorine, F<br>Atomic No. = 9 | Neon, Ne<br>Atomic No. = 10 | Sodium, Na<br>Atomic No. = 11 | Magnesium, Mg<br>Atomic No. = 12 |
| 2.7 | 2.8 | 2.8.1 | 2.8.2 |
| Aluminium, Al<br>Atomic No. = 13 | Silicon, Si<br>Atomic No. = 14 | Phosphorus, P<br>Atomic No. = 15 | Sulfur, S<br>Atomic No. = 16 |
| 2.8.3 | 2.8.4 | 2.8.5 | 2.8.6 |
| Chlorine, Cl<br>Atomic No. = 17 | Argon, Ar<br>Atomic No. = 18 | Potassium, K<br>Atomic No. = 19 | Calcium, Ca<br>Atomic No. = 20 |
| 2.8.7 | 2.8.8 | 2.8.8.1 | 2.8.8.2 |

## Quick Test

1. What particles are found in the nucleus of an atom?
2. What is an element?
3. a) What is the symbol for fluorine?
   b) What is the mass number of fluorine?
   c) What is the atomic number of fluorine?
   d) How many neutrons does an atom of fluorine have?

## Ions

An **ion** is a **charged atom** or group of atoms, e.g. $Na^+$, $Cl^-$, $NH_4^+$, $SO_4^{2-}$.

A **positive ion** is made when an atom, or group of atoms, **loses** one or more **electrons**. For example, losing two electrons makes a $2^+$ ion, e.g. $Mg^{2+}$.

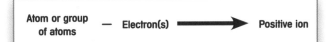

A **negative ion** is made when an atom, or group of atoms, **gains** one or more electrons. For example, gaining two electrons makes a $2^-$ ion, e.g. $O^{2-}$.

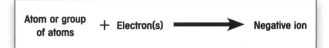

## Ionic Bonding

In **ionic bonding**:
- the metal atom loses all outer-shell **electrons** to become a **positive ion**
- the non-metal atom **gains electrons** to fill its outer shell and become a **negative ion**
- the positive and negative ions are attracted to each other. This attraction is an **ionic bond**.

Two ionically bonded compounds are **sodium chloride** and **magnesium oxide**. They have high melting points. They don't conduct electricity when solid.

But both of these compounds dissolve in water and **can conduct electricity** when **in solution**. They can also **conduct electricity** when **molten**.

## Structure and Physical Properties

Sodium chloride (NaCl) and magnesium oxide (MgO) form **giant ionic lattices** in which positive and negative ions are **strongly attracted** to each other.

(HT) This means that they:
- have high melting points as there is a strong attraction between oppositely charged ions
- can conduct electricity when molten or in solution because the charged ions are free to move about
- don't conduct electricity when solid, because the ions are held in place and can't move.

But magnesium oxide has a higher melting point than sodium chloride as the ionic bonds are stronger and need more energy to be broken.

In your exam you may be asked to predict the properties of other giant ionic structures. Use your knowledge about magnesium oxide and sodium chloride to help you.

**Sodium Chloride**

$Na^+$ ion, i.e. a sodium atom that has lost 1 electron
$Cl^-$ ion, i.e. a chlorine atom that has gained 1 electron

# C4 Ionic Bonding

## The Ionic Bond

When a metal and a non-metal combine, electrons are transferred from one **atom** to the other forming **ions**. Each ion will have a complete outer shell (**a stable octet**).

### (HT) Example 1 – Sodium chloride

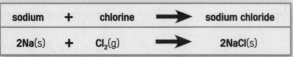

| sodium | + | chlorine | ⟶ | sodium chloride |
|--------|---|----------|---|-----------------|
| **2Na**(s) | + | **Cl₂**(g) | ⟶ | **2NaCl**(s) |

1. The sodium atom has 1 electron in its outer shell.
2. The electron is transferred to the chlorine atom. Both atoms now have 8 electrons in their outer shell (a stable octet).
3. The atoms become ions (Na⁺ and Cl⁻).
4. The compound formed is sodium chloride, NaCl.

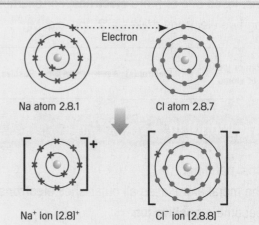

Na atom 2.8.1    Cl atom 2.8.7

Na⁺ ion [2.8]⁺    Cl⁻ ion [2.8.8]⁻

### Example 2 – Magnesium oxide

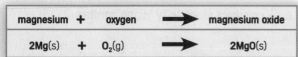

| magnesium | + | oxygen | ⟶ | magnesium oxide |
|-----------|---|--------|---|-----------------|
| **2Mg**(s) | + | **O₂**(g) | ⟶ | **2MgO**(s) |

1. The magnesium atom has 2 electrons in its outer shell.
2. The 2 electrons are transferred to the oxygen atom. Both atoms now have 8 electrons in their outer shell (a stable octet).
3. The atoms become ions (Mg²⁺ and O²⁻).
4. The compound formed is magnesium oxide, MgO.

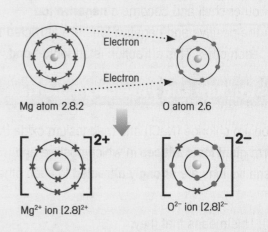

Mg atom 2.8.2    O atom 2.6

Mg²⁺ ion [2.8]²⁺    O²⁻ ion [2.8]²⁻

### Example 3 – Sodium oxide

| sodium | + | oxygen | ⟶ | sodium oxide |
|--------|---|--------|---|--------------|
| **4Na**(s) | + | **O₂**(g) | ⟶ | **2Na₂O**(s) |

1. The sodium atom has 1 electron in its outer shell.
2. An oxygen atom needs 2 electrons, so 2 Na atoms are needed.
3. The atoms become ions (Na⁺, Na⁺ and O²⁻).
4. The compound formed is sodium oxide, Na₂O.

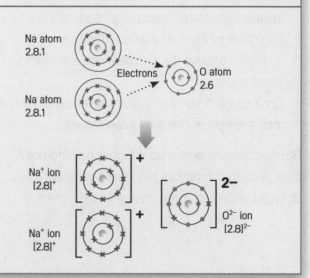

Na atom 2.8.1

Na atom 2.8.1

Electrons    O atom 2.6

Na⁺ ion [2.8]⁺

Na⁺ ion [2.8]⁺

O²⁻ ion [2.8]²⁻

## HT The Ionic Bond (Cont.)

### Example 4 – Magnesium chloride

| magnesium | + | chlorine | $\longrightarrow$ | magnesium chloride |
|---|---|---|---|---|
| $Mg(s)$ | + | $Cl_2(g)$ | $\longrightarrow$ | $MgCl_2(g)$ |

1. The magnesium atom has 2 electrons in its outer shell.
2. A chlorine atom only needs 1 electron, so 2 Cl atoms are needed.
3. The atoms become ions ($Mg^{2+}$, $Cl^-$ and $Cl^-$).
4. The compound formed is magnesium chloride, $MgCl_2$.

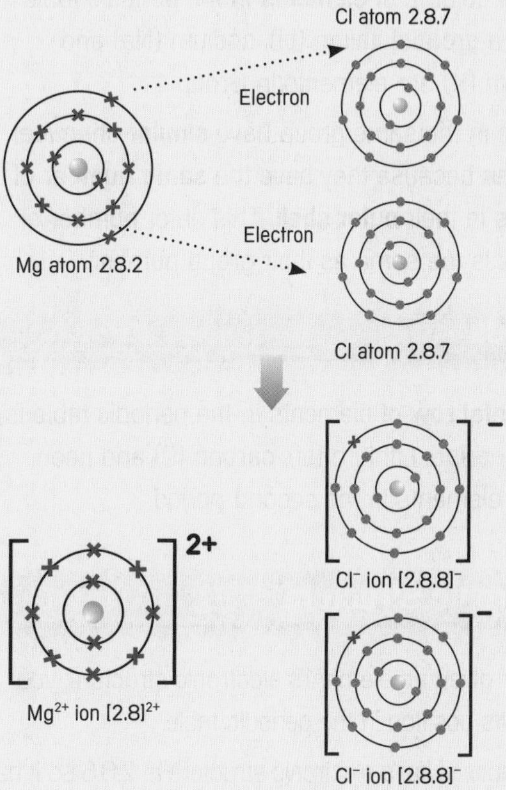

Cl atom 2.8.7

Electron

Mg atom 2.8.2

Electron

Cl atom 2.8.7

$Mg^{2+}$ ion $[2.8]^{2+}$

$Cl^-$ ion $[2.8.8]^-$

$Cl^-$ ion $[2.8.8]^-$

## Formulae of Ionic Compounds

Ions with different charges combine to form **ionic compounds** which have **equal amounts** of **positive** and **negative** charge.

| Positive Ions | | | | | | Negative Ions |
|---|---|---|---|---|---|---|
| 1+ e.g. $K^+$, $Na^+$ | | 2+ e.g. $Mg^{2+}$, $Cu^{2+}$ | | 3+ e.g. $Al^{3+}$, $Fe^{3+}$ | | |
| KCl 1+ ↘ 1– | NaOH 1+ ↘ 1– | $MgCl_2$ 2+ ↘ 2 × 1– = 2– | $Cu(OH)_2$ 2+ ↘ 2 × 1– = 2– | $AlCl_3$ 3+ ↘ 3 × 1– = 3– | $Fe(OH)_3$ 3+ ↘ 3 × 1– = 3– | 1– e.g. $Cl^-$, $OH^-$ |
| $K_2SO_4$ 2 × 1+ = 2+ ↘ 2– | $Na_2O$ 2 × 1+ = 2+ ↘ 2– | $MgSO_4$ 2+ ↘ 2– | CuO 2+ ↘ 2– | $Al_2(SO_4)_3$ 2 × 3+ = 6+ ↘ 3 × 2– = 6– | $Fe_2O_3$ 2 × 3+ = 6+ ↘ 3 × 2– = 6– | 2– e.g. $SO_4^{2-}$, $O^{2-}$ |

# C4 The Periodic Table and Covalent Bonding

## Groups

A vertical column of **elements** in the periodic table is called a **group**. Lithium (Li), sodium (Na) and potassium (K) are elements in Group 1.

Elements in the same group have **similar chemical properties** because they have the **same number** of **electrons** in their **outer shell**. This outer number of electrons is the same as their group number.

For example:

- Group 1 elements have one electron in their outer shell.
- Group 7 elements have seven electrons in their outer shell.
- Group O elements have a full outer shell.

## Periods

A **horizontal row** of elements in the periodic table is called a **period**. Lithium (Li), carbon (C) and neon (Ne) are elements in the second period.

The **period** for an element is related to the number of **occupied electron shells** it has. For example, sodium (Na), aluminium (Al) and chlorine (Cl) have three shells of electrons so they are in the third period.

## Electronic Structure

If you are given an element's electronic structure, you can find its position in the periodic table.

For example, sulfur's electronic structure is 2.8.6 so it has:

- three electron shells, so it can be found in the **third period**
- six electrons in its outer shell, so it can be found in **Group 6**.

## Bonding

There are three types of bonding:

- **Ionic bonding** between metals and non-metals.
- **Covalent bonding** between non-metals.
- Metallic bonding for metals only.

## Covalent Bonding

Covalent bonding is when **non-metals** combine by **sharing pairs** of **electrons**. Water and carbon dioxide are both covalently bonded molecules. Water ($H_2O$) contains hydrogen and oxygen atoms. It:

- is a liquid at room temperature and has a low melting point
- doesn't conduct electricity.

One molecule of water is made up of one atom of oxygen and two atoms of hydrogen.

Carbon dioxide ($CO_2$) contains carbon and oxygen atoms. Carbon dioxide:

- is a gas at room temperature and has a low melting point

- doesn't conduct electricity.

One molecule of carbon dioxide is made up of **one atom of carbon** and **two atoms of oxygen**.

Simple covalently bonded molecules, e.g. water and carbon dioxide have **weak intermolecular** forces of attraction between molecules.

(HT) Simple covalently bonded molecules have low melting points because they have weak intermolecular forces of attraction between molecules. They don't conduct electricity because there aren't any free electrons.

Group • Period • Covalent bonding

## HT Representing Molecules

You should be familiar with how simple covalently bonded molecules are formed.

**Hydrogen (H₂)** – the two hydrogen atoms share a pair of electrons.

**Chlorine (Cl₂)** – the two chlorine atoms share a pair of electrons.

**Methane (CH₄)** – the carbon atom shares a pair of electrons with each hydrogen atom.

**Carbon dioxide (CO₂)** – the outer shells of the carbon and oxygen atoms overlap. The carbon atom shares two pairs of electrons with each oxygen atom to form a double covalently bonded molecule.

**Water (H₂O)** – the outer shells of the hydrogen and oxygen atoms overlap. The oxygen atom shares a pair of electrons with each hydrogen atom to form a water molecule.

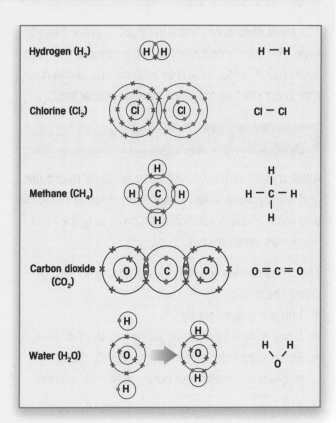

## Development of the Periodic Table

Many people have researched the properties of elements and tried to classify them.

**Dobereiner** was the first to suggest a **Law of Triads**, where he grouped the elements into sets of three with similar properties. The middle element would have the average mass of the other two elements. But not all the elements were known and the pattern did not work for every known element.

**John Newlands** was the first scientist to make a table of elements, which he called the **Law of Octaves**, where every eighth element behaved the same. But he included some compounds in his table as he believed them to be elements.

**Mendeleev** was the author of the modern periodic table.

HT Mendeleev left gaps in his table for the unknown elements and made predictions about their properties. His predictions were later proved correct. Also, investigations on atomic structure agreed with his ideas.

### Quick Test

1. Explain how sodium atoms become sodium ions.
2. What is an ionic bond?
3. Magnesium oxide is an ionic compound.
   a) When can this compound conduct electricity?
   b) What is the formula of this compound?
4. What is a covalent bond?

# C4 The Group 1 Elements

## Group 1 – The Alkali Metals

The **alkali metals** are found in Group 1 of the periodic table. The first three elements in the group are lithium, sodium and potassium. They all have one electron in their outer shell so they have **similar properties**.

Alkali metals are stored **under oil** because they:
- react with air
- react vigorously with water.

## Reactions with Water

Alkali metals react with water to produce **hydrogen** and a **hydroxide**. Alkali metal hydroxides are soluble and form alkaline solutions, which is why they are known as **alkali** metals.

The alkali metals react more vigorously as you go down the group:
- Lithium reacts gently.
- Sodium reacts more aggressively than lithium.
- Potassium reacts more aggressively than sodium – it melts and burns with a lilac flame.

You may be asked to predict the properties of rubidium and caesium. Use your knowledge of other alkali metals to help you.

lithium + water → lithium hydroxide + hydrogen

$$2Li(s) + 2H_2O(l) \rightarrow 2LiOH(aq) + H_2(g)$$

sodium + water → sodium hydroxide + hydrogen

$$2Na(s) + 2H_2O(l) \rightarrow 2NaOH(aq) + H_2(g)$$

potassium + water → potassium hydroxide + hydrogen

$$2K(s) + 2H_2O(l) \rightarrow 2KOH(aq) + H_2(g)$$

## Flame Tests

Lithium, sodium and potassium compounds can be recognised by the colours they make in a **flame test**.

1. A piece of clean nichrome wire is dipped in water.
2. The wire is dipped in the solid compound (known as the sample). The wire is then put into a Bunsen flame.
3. Each compound will produce a different coloured flame.

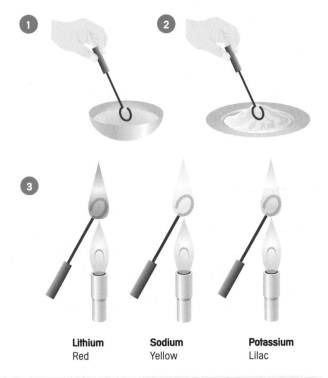

**Lithium** Red    **Sodium** Yellow    **Potassium** Lilac

**Key Words**      Hydroxide

## HT Properties of the Alkali Metals

Alkali metals have similar chemical and physical properties.

Rubidium is the fourth element in Group 1. Rubidium's reaction with water is:

- very fast
- **exothermic** (gives out energy)
- violent (if it's carried out in a glass beaker, the beaker may shatter).

Density increases as you go down the group (with the exception of potassium). Caesium has the greatest density, and lowest melting and boiling points.

| Element | Symbol | Melting Point (°C) | Boiling Point (°C) | Density (g/cm³) |
|---------|--------|--------------------|--------------------|-----------------|
| Lithium | Li | 180 | 1340 | 0.53 |
| Sodium | Na | 98 | 883 | 0.97 |
| Potassium | K | 64 | 760 | 0.86 |
| Rubidium | Rb | 39 | 688 | 1.53 |
| Caesium | Cs | 29 | 671 | 1.90 |

## Trends in Group 1

Alkali metals have similar chemical properties because as they react, each atom **loses** one **electron** from its outer shell. So, a **positive ion** with a stable electronic structure is made.

The alkali metals become **more reactive** as you go down the group because the outer shell gets **further away** from the positive attraction of the **nucleus**. This makes it easier for an atom to lose an electron from its outer shell.

The equations for the formation of the Group 1 metal ions are:

| | |
|---|---|
| Li | $\longrightarrow$ Li⁺ + e⁻ |
| Na | $\longrightarrow$ Na⁺ + e⁻ |
| K | $\longrightarrow$ K⁺ + e⁻ |

**Oxidation** involves the loss of electrons by an atom. If the ionic equation for a reaction shows that an electron has been lost, an oxidation reaction took place.

**Examples of Oxidation**

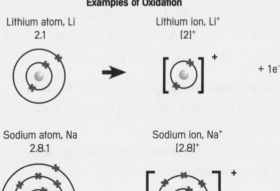

Lithium atom, Li
2.1

Lithium ion, Li⁺
[2]⁺

+ 1e⁻

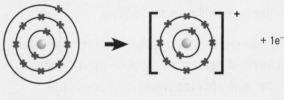

Sodium atom, Na
2.8.1

Sodium ion, Na⁺
[2.8]⁺

+ 1e⁻

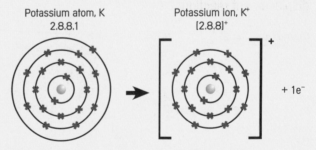

Potassium atom, K
2.8.8.1

Potassium ion, K⁺
[2.8.8]⁺

+ 1e⁻

## Quick Test

1 Why do Group 1 metals have similar chemical properties?
2 What colour is a flame when a lithium compound is added?

# C4 The Group 7 Elements

## Group 7 – The Halogens

The five non-metals in Group 7 are known as the **halogens**. They all have seven electrons in their outer shell so they have similar chemical properties.

Fluorine, chlorine, bromine and iodine are halogens. At room temperature:

- chlorine is a green gas
- bromine is an orange liquid
- iodine is a grey solid.

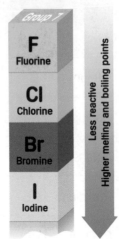

The halogens have many uses:

- **Iodine** is used as an **antiseptic** to sterilise wounds.
- **Chlorine** is used to **sterilise water**, to make **pesticides** and to make **plastics**.

Halogens react vigorously with **alkali metals** to form metal **halides**, for example:

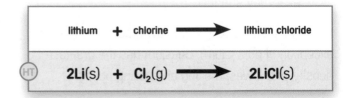

$$\text{lithium} + \text{chlorine} \longrightarrow \text{lithium chloride}$$

(HT) $$2Li(s) + Cl_2(g) \longrightarrow 2LiCl(s)$$

## Displacement Reactions

The reactivity of the halogens decreases as you go down the group. So, fluorine is the most reactive halogen and iodine is the least reactive.

A **more reactive** halogen will **displace** a **less reactive** halogen from an aqueous solution of its metal halide. For example:

- chlorine will displace bromides and iodides
- bromine will displace iodides.

If chlorine gas was passed through an aqueous solution of potassium bromide, bromine and potassium chloride would be made in the displacement reaction.

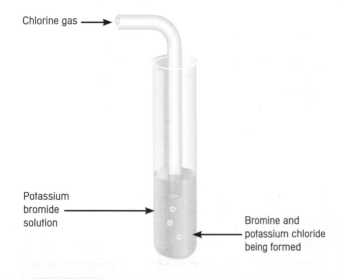

The products of reactions between halogens and aqueous solutions of salts are as follows:

| Halogen \ Halide salt | Potassium Chloride, KCl | Potassium Bromide, KBr | Potassium Iodide, KI |
|---|---|---|---|
| Chlorine, Cl$_2$ | No reaction | Potassium chloride + bromine | Potassium chloride + iodine |
| Bromine, Br$_2$ | No reaction | No reaction | Potassium bromide + iodine |
| Iodine, I$_2$ | No reaction | No reaction | No reaction |

$$\text{potassium bromide} + \text{chlorine} \longrightarrow \text{potassium chloride} + \text{bromine}$$

(HT) $$2KBr(aq) + Cl_2(g) \longrightarrow 2KCl(aq) + Br_2(aq)$$

$$\text{potassium iodide} + \text{chlorine} \longrightarrow \text{potassium chloride} + \text{iodine}$$

(HT) $$2KI(aq) + Cl_2(g) \longrightarrow 2KCl(aq) + I_2(aq)$$

$$\text{potassium iodide} + \text{bromine} \longrightarrow \text{potassium bromide} + \text{iodine}$$

(HT) $$2KI(aq) + Br_2(l) \longrightarrow 2KBr(aq) + I_2(aq)$$

You make be asked to suggest if a displacement reaction will happen. Remember that chlorine is more reactive than bromine, which is more reactive than iodine.

**Key Words**         Halogen • Halide

## Properties of the Halogens

The physical and chemical properties of the halogens change as you go down the group.

**Fluorine** is the most reactive element in the group. It will **displace** all of the other halogens from an aqueous solution of their metal halides.

**Astatine** is a semi-metallic, radioactive element and only very small amounts are found naturally. It's the least reactive of the halogens and, theoretically, it would be unable to displace any of the other halogens from an aqueous solution of their metal halides.

Astatine is very unstable and difficult to study. So, the information for astatine is estimated by looking at the trend in boiling point, melting point and density as you go down Group 7.

| Element | Symbol | Melting Point (°C) | Boiling Point (°C) | Density (g/cm³) |
|---------|--------|--------------------|--------------------|------------------|
| Fluorine | F | −220 | −188 | 0.0016 |
| Chlorine | Cl | −101 | −34 | 0.003 |
| Bromine | Br | −7 | 59 | 3.12 |
| Iodine | I | 114 | 184 | 4.95 |
| Astatine | At | 302 (estimated) | 337 (estimated) | 7 (estimated) |

## Trends in Group 7

The halogens have similar chemical properties because, as they react, each atom **gains** one **electron** to form a **negative** ion with a stable electronic structure.

**Reduction** involves the gain of electrons by an atom, for example:

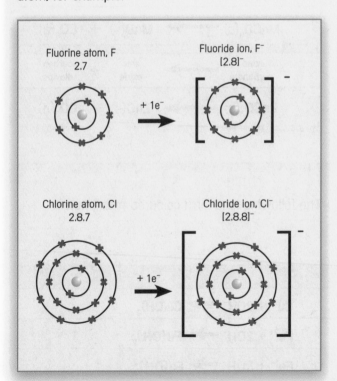

Fluorine atom, F
2.7

+ 1e⁻

Fluoride ion, F⁻
[2.8]⁻

Chlorine atom, Cl
2.8.7

+ 1e⁻

Chloride ion, Cl⁻
[2.8.8]⁻

The halogens at the top of the group are **more reactive** than those at the bottom of the group because the outer shell is **closer** to the **positive attraction** of the **nucleus**. This makes it **easier** for an atom to **gain an electron**.

Equations for the formation of the halide **ions** from halogen molecules are:

$$F_2 + 2e^- \longrightarrow 2F^-$$

$$Cl_2 + 2e^- \longrightarrow 2Cl^-$$

By looking at an equation of a reaction, you can decide whether it is **oxidation** or **reduction**:

- If **electrons** are **added**, it's a **reduction** reaction.
- If **electrons** are **taken away**, it's an **oxidation** reaction.

So, the reactions shown above are reduction reactions.

An easy way to remember the definitions of oxidation and reduction is by remembering **OILRIG**:

- **O**xidation **I**s **L**oss of electrons.
- **R**eduction **I**s **G**ain of electrons.

# C4 Transition Elements

## The Transition Metals

The **transition metals**, a block of metallic elements, are between Groups 2 and 3 of the periodic table. This block includes iron (Fe), copper (Cu), platinum (Pt), mercury (Hg), chromium (Cr) and zinc (Zn).

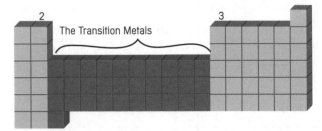

The Transition Metals

Transition metals have the typical properties of metals. Their compounds are often coloured, for example:

- **copper** compounds are **blue**
- **iron(II)** compounds are **light green**
- **iron(III)** compounds are **orange–brown**.

Many transition metals and their compounds are catalysts, for example:

- iron is used in the Haber process
- nickel is used in the manufacture of margarine.

## Thermal Decomposition

**Thermal decomposition** is a reaction where a substance is broken down into two or more substances by heating.

When **transition metal carbonates** are heated, a **colour change** happens. They decompose (break down) to form a **metal oxide** and **carbon dioxide**. The test for carbon dioxide is that it **turns limewater milky**.

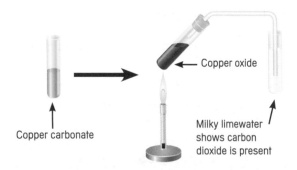

Copper carbonate

Copper oxide

Milky limewater shows carbon dioxide is present

| copper(II) carbonate | → | copper(II) oxide | + | carbon dioxide |

(HT) $CuCO_3(s) \longrightarrow CuO(s) + CO_2(g)$

| iron(II) carbonate | → | iron(II) oxide | + | carbon dioxide |

(HT) $FeCO_3(s) \longrightarrow FeO(s) + CO_2(g)$

| manganese carbonate | → | manganese oxide | + | carbon dioxide |

(HT) $MnCO_3(s) \longrightarrow MnO(s) + CO_2(g)$

| zinc carbonate | → | zinc oxide | + | carbon dioxide |

(HT) $ZnCO_3(s) \longrightarrow ZnO(s) + CO_2(g)$

## Identifying Transition Metal Ions

**Precipitation** is the reaction between **solutions** that makes an **insoluble solid**. The insoluble solid is known as a precipitate.

The following ions form coloured **precipitates**:

| Metal Ion | Symbol | Colour | Equation |
|---|---|---|---|
| Copper(II) | $Cu^{2+}$ | Blue | (HT) $Cu^{2+} + 2OH^- \longrightarrow Cu(OH)_2$ |
| Iron(II) | $Fe^{2+}$ | Grey-green | (HT) $Fe^{2+} + 2OH^- \longrightarrow Fe(OH)_2$ |
| Iron(III) | $Fe^{3+}$ | Orange | (HT) $Fe^{3+} + 3OH^- \longrightarrow Fe(OH)_3$ |

# Metal Structure and Properties C4

## Metals

Transition metals have many uses, for example:

- **Iron** is used to make steel (which is used to make cars and bridges because it's very strong).
- **Copper** is used to make electrical wiring because it's a good conductor.

Metals are very useful materials because of their properties. Several of their properties include:

- They're **lustrous**, e.g. gold is used in jewellery.
- They're **hard** and have a **high density**, e.g. steel is used to make drill parts.
- They have **high tensile strength** (able to bear loads), e.g. steel is used to make bridge girders.
- They have **high melting** and **boiling points**, e.g. tungsten is used to make light-bulb filaments.
- They're **good conductors** of **heat** and **electricity**, e.g. copper is used to make pans and wiring.

## Structure of Metals

Metal atoms are packed very close together in a regular arrangement. The atoms are held together by **metallic bonds**.

Metals have **high melting and boiling points** because lots of energy is needed to break the strong metallic bonds. As the metal atoms pack together, they build a structure of crystals.

(HT) Metal crystals are made from closely packed positive metal ions in a 'sea' of **delocalised** (free) electrons. The **free movement** of the electrons allows the metal to **conduct electricity**.

The metal is held together by **strong forces** called metallic bonds. These are the electrostatic attractions between the metal ions and the delocalised electrons. So the metals have high melting and boiling points.

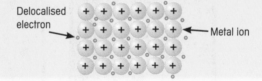

Delocalised electron      Metal ion

## Superconductors

Metals are able to conduct electricity because the electrons flow easily through them, moving from atom to atom. At low temperatures, some metals can become **superconductors**.

A superconductor has little, or no, resistance to the flow of electricity. This low resistance is useful for:

- powerful electromagnets, e.g. inside medical scanners
- very fast electronic circuits, e.g. in a supercomputer
- power transmission that doesn't lose energy.

(HT) The disadvantage of current superconductors is that they only work at temperatures **below −200°C**. This very low temperature is **costly** to maintain and impractical for large-scale uses. So, there is a need to develop superconductors that will work at room temperature (20°C).

### Quick Test

1. Why do Group 7 metals have similar chemical properties?
2. Which transition metal is used as a catalyst in the Haber process?
3. What is a thermal decomposition reaction?

# C4 Purifying and Testing Water

## Water

The four main sources of water in the UK are:
- rivers
- lakes
- reservoirs
- aquifers (wells and bore holes).

Water is an important resource for industry as well as being essential for drinking, washing, etc. The **chemical industry** uses water:
- as a coolant
- as a solvent
- as a raw material.

In some parts of Britain, the **demand** for water is **higher than the supply**, so it's important to **conserve** and not waste water.

Many parts of the developing world don't have access to clean water (water without disease-carrying microorganisms). The World Health Organisation estimates that:
- over 2 million people worldwide die every year from water-borne diseases
- nearly 20% of the world's population doesn't have access to clean drinking water.

## Water Treatment

**Water Treatment Process**

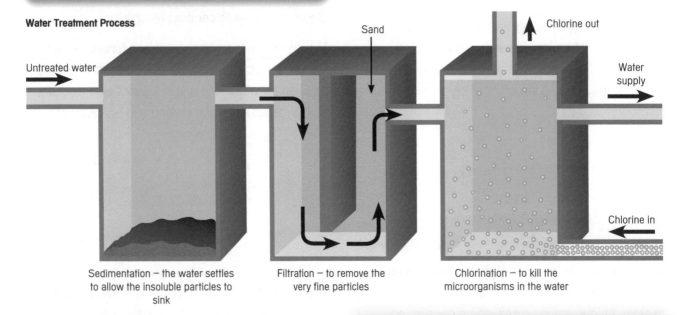

Sedimentation – the water settles to allow the insoluble particles to sink

Filtration – to remove the very fine particles

Chlorination – to kill the microorganisms in the water

Water has to be treated to purify it and make it safe to drink. Untreated (raw) water can contain:
- **insoluble** particles
- pollutants
- microorganisms
- dissolved **salts** and minerals.

(HT) Tap water isn't pure – it contains soluble materials that aren't removed by the normal water treatment process. Some of these materials could be poisonous, so extra steps must be taken to remove them.

To obtain pure water, it must be distilled, but this process uses a lot of energy and is expensive.

The equipment and energy needed to **distil sea water** is very expensive. The cost of making drinking water out of sea water is currently too high to make it a realistic option in the UK.

Insoluble • Salt • Distillation

## Pollutants in Water

**Pollutants** that can be found in water supplies are often difficult to remove. They include:

- **nitrates** from the run-off of fertilisers
- **lead compounds** from old pipes in the plumbing
- **pesticides** from spraying crops near to the water supply.

## Dissolved Ions

The dissolved **ions** of some salts are easy to identify as they will undergo **precipitation** reactions. A precipitation reaction occurs when an insoluble solid is made from mixing two solutions together.

Sulfates can be detected using barium chloride solution – a white precipitate of barium sulfate forms. For example:

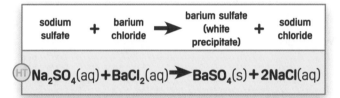

$$Na_2SO_4(aq) + BaCl_2(aq) \rightarrow BaSO_4(s) + 2NaCl(aq)$$

Silver nitrate solution is used to detect **halide ions**. Halides are the ions made by the halogens (Group 7).

With silver nitrate:

- chlorides form a white precipitate
- bromides form a cream precipitate
- iodides form a pale yellow precipitate.

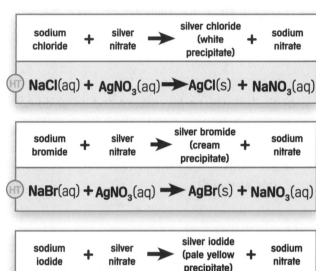

$$NaCl(aq) + AgNO_3(aq) \rightarrow AgCl(s) + NaNO_3(aq)$$

$$NaBr(aq) + AgNO_3(aq) \rightarrow AgBr(s) + NaNO_3(aq)$$

$$NaI(aq) + AgNO_3(aq) \rightarrow AgI(s) + NaNO_3(aq)$$

## Interpreting Data

In your exam, you may be asked to interpret data about water resources in the UK. For example, this table shows some pollutants and the maximum amounts allowed in drinking water.

You don't have to remember the data, but you might, for example, be asked to pick out which pollutant has the smallest allowed concentration, or transfer this data onto a graph.

| Pollutant | Maximum Amount Allowed |
|---|---|
| Nitrates | 50 parts in 1 000 000 000 parts water |
| Lead | 50 parts in 1 000 000 000 parts water |
| Pesticides | 0.5 parts in 1 000 000 000 parts water |

### Quick Test

1. Where does the nitrate water pollution come from?
2. Dissolved ions can be identified using precipitation reactions.
   a) What chemical is used to identify sulfates?
   b) Write a word equation for the reaction between silver nitrate and sodium chloride.
3. Water must be treated so that it is safe to drink.
   a) What does the sedimentation process do?
   b) What chemical is added to the water to kill microorganisms?

# C4 Exam Practice Questions

1 Sodium metal can react with chlorine gas to make sodium chloride.

**a)** What is an ion? [1]

_____

**b)** How would you make a 1⁻ ion from a neutral atom? [1]

_____

**c)** Give the properties of a typical ionic substance such as sodium chloride. [3]

_____

2 There are about 100 naturally occurring elements. They are all listed in the periodic table.

**a)** What type of elements usually bond covalently? [1]

_____

**b)** Explain why carbon dioxide and water do not conduct electricity. [1]

_____

**c)** An element has the electronic structure 2.8.4. In which group and period would you find this element? [1]

_____

**d)** Alkali metals are found in Group 1 of the periodic table. These metals all have 1 electron in their outer shell. Why are Group 1 metals stored in oil? [2]

_____

**e)** Write the word equation for the reaction between lithium and water. [2]

_____

3 Atoms often form bonds so that they have a complete outer shell of electrons.

**a)** What type of chemical bonding shares electron pairs? [1]

_____

**b)** How many atoms of each element are there in $Mg(NO_3)_2$? [1]

_____

_____

**c)** Balance the following equation:

$Na + H_2O \rightarrow NaOH + H_2$ [1]

4 When some metal carbonates are heated they undergo a chemical change.

   **a)** What is thermal decomposition? [2]

   _____

   **b)** Write the word equation for the thermal decomposition of copper carbonate. [2]

   _____

   **c)** Which metal ion makes an orange–brown precipitate with sodium hydroxide solution? [1]

   _____

5 Halogens are the elements found in Group 7 of the periodic table.

   **a)** Which gas is used to sterilise water? _____ [1]

   **b)** Write the word equation to show the reaction of sodium iodide solution with chlorine gas. [2]

   _____

HT

   **c)** Write the balanced symbol equation to show the reaction of sodium iodide solution with chlorine gas. [2]

   _____

   **d)** Write the ionic equation to show the formation of bromide ions from a bromine molecule. [2]

   _____

6 Halogens are found in Group 7 of the periodic table. Explain why halogens have similar properties and describe the trend in reactivity as you go down the group. [6]

   ✎ *The quality of your written communication will be assessed in your answer to this question.*

   _____

   _____

   _____

   _____

   _____

   _____

   _____

   _____

   _____

# P3 Speed

## Measuring Speed

The **speed** of an object is a measure of how fast it's moving. Speed is measured in:
- metres per second (m/s)
- kilometres per hour (km/h)
- miles per hour (mph).

You can work out the speed of a moving object if you know:
- the **distance** it travels (measured using a measuring tape/trundle wheel)
- the **time it takes** to travel that distance (measured using a stopwatch/stopclock).

The faster the speed of an object:
- the greater the distance it travels in a particular time
- the shorter the time it takes to travel a particular distance.

You can calculate the speed of an object by using this formula:

$$\text{Speed} = \frac{\text{Distance travelled}}{\text{Time taken}}$$

$$\frac{d}{s \times t}$$

The speed may change over a given distance so the average distance over the whole journey is used.

$$\text{Distance} = \text{Average speed} \times \text{Time} = \left(\frac{u + v}{2}\right) \times t$$

where u is initial speed and v is final speed

### Example 1

Calculate the speed of a cyclist who travels 2400m in 5 minutes.

$$\text{Speed} = \frac{\text{Distance}}{\text{Time taken}}$$

$$= \frac{2400m}{300s} = \textbf{8m/s}$$

You can rearrange the speed formula to calculate either distance or time taken.

### Example 2

Calculate the distance a car travels in 90 minutes if it's travelling at a constant speed of 80km/h.

$$\text{Distance} = \text{Speed} \times \text{Time taken}$$

$$= 80km/h \times 1.5h = \textbf{120km}$$

### Example 3

Calculate the time it takes a motorcyclist to travel a distance of 120km at 50km/h.

$$\text{Time taken} = \frac{\text{Distance}}{\text{Speed}}$$

$$= \frac{120km}{50km/h} = 2.4 \text{ hours} = \textbf{2h 24min}$$

## Speed Cameras

Speed cameras generally take **two pictures** of a vehicle a **certain amount of time apart**. The position of the vehicle in relation to the **distance markings** on the road in the two pictures can be used to calculate the vehicle's speed.

$$\text{Speed of car} = \frac{\text{Distance travelled between pictures}}{\text{Time taken between first and second picture}}$$

## Distance–Time Graphs

The slope of a **distance–time graph** represents the **speed** of an object. The **steeper the gradient** (**slope**), the **greater the speed**.

This graph shows the movement of three people.

**1** A stationary person standing 10m from point (0).

**2** A person moving at a constant speed of 2m/s.

**3** A person moving at a greater constant speed of 3m/s.

**4** A person moving at the same speed as **2** but in the opposite direction. This graph will have the same gradient but will slope in the opposite direction.

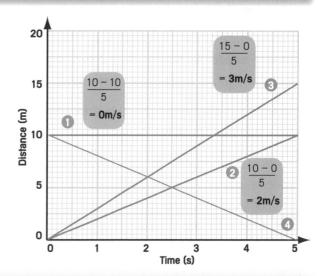

## HT Calculating Speed

To work out the speed of an object, take any two points on a distance–time graph and read off the distance travelled for that part of the journey, and the time taken to get there (see Graph 1).

By looking at the graph, you can use the formula to calculate the speed at each part of the journey.

**0 to A:** Speed $= \dfrac{15 - 0m}{3s} = $ **5m/s**

**A to B:** Speed $= \dfrac{15 - 15m}{5s} = $ **0m/s**

**B to C:** Speed $= \dfrac{0 - 15m}{4s} = $ **−3.75m/s**

Negative sign shows that the object is moving in the reverse direction, i.e. back towards the starting point.

So, the object:

- travelled at 5m/s for 3 seconds
- remained stationary for 5 seconds
- travelled at 3.75m/s for 4 seconds back to the starting point.

Graphs can also be drawn for **non-uniform speed** (see Graph 2).

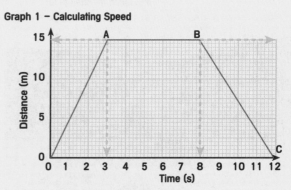

Graph 1 – Calculating Speed

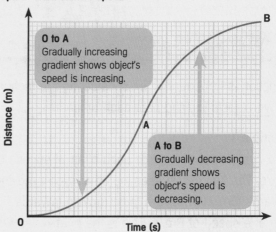

Graph 2 – Non-uniform Speed

**0 to A**
Gradually increasing gradient shows object's speed is increasing.

**A to B**
Gradually decreasing gradient shows object's speed is decreasing.

## Quick Test

**1** What two quantities are needed to calculate speed?

**2** What does the gradient of a distance–time graph represent?

**Key Words**          Distance–Time graph

# P3 Changing Speed

## Measuring Acceleration

The **acceleration** or **deceleration** of an object is the change in **speed** per second. It's a measure of how quickly an object **speeds up** or **slows down**.

Acceleration is **only** measured in **metres per second squared** (m/s²).

To work out the acceleration of a moving object you need to know:

- the **change in speed**
- the **time taken** for the change in speed.

You can calculate the acceleration (or deceleration) of an object by using this formula:

$$\text{Acceleration (m/s}^2) = \frac{\text{Change in speed (m/s)}}{\text{Time taken for change (s)}}$$

### Example 1

A cyclist accelerates uniformly from rest and reaches a speed of 10m/s after 5 seconds. He then decelerates uniformly and comes to rest in a further 10 seconds.

**a)** Calculate his acceleration.

$$\text{Acceleration} = \frac{\text{Change in Speed}}{\text{Time taken for change}}$$

$$= \frac{10 - 0\text{m/s}}{5\text{s}} = \textbf{2m/s}^2$$

**b)** Calculate his deceleration (negative acceleration).

$$= \frac{0 - 10\text{m/s}}{10\text{s}} = \textbf{-1m/s}^2 \textbf{ accleration}$$

$$= \textbf{1m/s}^2 \textbf{ deceleration}$$

(HT) The acceleration formula can be rearranged to calculate time taken or change in speed.

### Example 2

A car accelerates at 1.5m/s² for 12 seconds. Calculate the change in speed of the car.

$$\text{Change in speed} = \text{Acceleration} \times \text{Time taken}$$

$$= 1.5\text{m/s}^2 \times 12\text{s} = \textbf{18m/s}$$

*N.B. Acceleration can involve a **change of direction** as well as **speed**. It is a **vector quantity**.*

## Relative Speed

Direction is important when considering the motion of two objects moving near each other.

### Example 1

Two cyclists move towards each other at speeds of 4m/s. The first cyclist sees the other cyclist moving towards him. He appears to be moving towards him at a speed of 8m/s. This is the relative speed.

### Example 2

Two cyclists are moving in the same direction. The cyclist at the front appears to be moving away from the other cyclist at a relative speed of 2m/s, increasing the gap between them.

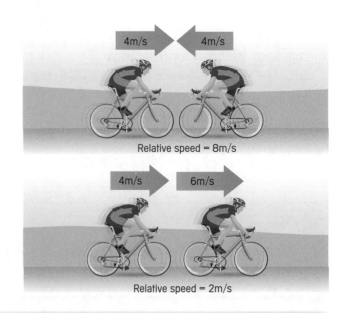

Relative speed = 8m/s

Relative speed = 2m/s

## Speed–Time Graphs

The slope of a **speed–time graph** represents the **acceleration** of the object. A constant acceleration increases the speed.

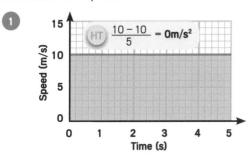

This graph shows an object moving at a constant speed of 10m/s. It **isn't** accelerating.

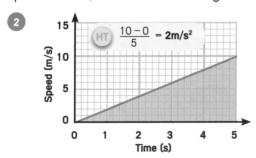

This graph shows an object moving at a constant acceleration of 2m/s².

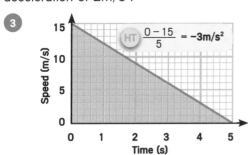

This graph shows an object moving at a constant acceleration of −3m/s².

*N.B. The **area underneath the line** in a speed–time graph represents the **total distance travelled**.*

### Quick Test

1. State the equation used to calculate acceleration.
2. What does an acceleration of −5m/s² tell you about the motion of the object?

(HT) To work out the acceleration of an object, take any two points on a speed–time graph and read off the change in speed over the chosen period, and the time taken for this change.

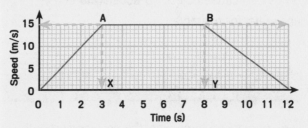

You can use the formula to calculate the acceleration at each part of the journey.

**O to A:** Acceleration $= \dfrac{15m/s - 0m/s}{3s} = $ **5m/s²**

**A to B:** Acceleration $= \dfrac{15m/s - 15m/s}{5s} = $ **0m/s²**

**B to C:** Acceleration $= \dfrac{0m/s - 15m/s}{4s} = $ **−3.75m/s²**

So, the object:
- accelerated at 5m/s² for 3 seconds
- travelled at a constant speed of 15m/s for 5 seconds
- decelerated at a rate of 3.75m/s² for 4 seconds.

> The total distance travelled can be calculated by working out the area under the speed–time graph.

= Area of OAX + Area of ABYX + Area of BCY

$= (\frac{1}{2} \times 3 \times 15) + (5 \times 15) + (\frac{1}{2} \times 4 \times 15) = $ **127.5m**

Graphs can also be drawn to represent **non-uniform** motion.

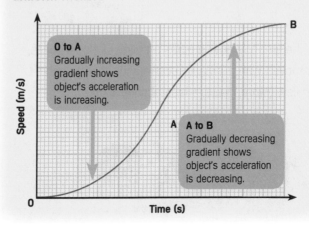

## Forces in Action

Forces, measured in **newtons (N)**, are **pushes** or **pulls**. They may be **different in size** and **act in different directions**.

Forces can cause objects to **accelerate** or decelerate, for example:

- **Weight** causes an apple falling from a tree to speed up as it falls.
- **Friction** causes a car to slow down.
- **Air resistance** causes a skydiver to slow down a lot when the parachute opens. If air resistance and weight are balanced, the skydiver stays at the same speed.

## Force, Mass and Acceleration

If an unbalanced force acts, the acceleration of the object will depend on:
- the force applied to the object
- the **mass** of the object.

**Example**
A boy pushes a trolley. He exerts an unbalanced force which causes the trolley to move and accelerate.

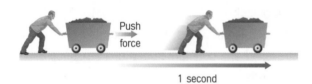
1 second

If two boys push the same trolley, it moves with a greater acceleration. (**More force = more acceleration.**)

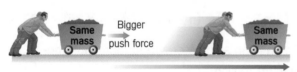
1 second

If the first boy now pushes a trolley of bigger mass, it moves with a smaller acceleration than the first trolley. (**More mass = less acceleration.**)

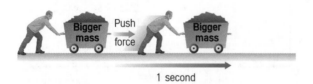
1 second

If two trolleys with different masses move with a constant acceleration, the trolley with the larger mass will have to be pushed with more force than the trolley with the smaller mass. (**More mass = more force required.**)

The relationship between force, mass and acceleration is shown in this formula:

| Resultant force (N) | = | Mass (kg) | × | Acceleration (m/s$^2$) |
| --- | --- | --- | --- | --- |

A **newton (N)** can be defined as the force needed to give a **mass of one kilogram** an acceleration of one **metre per second per second** ($1\,\text{m/s}^2$).

**Example**
A trolley of mass 400kg is accelerating at $0.5\,\text{m/s}^2$. What force is needed to achieve this acceleration?

Force = Mass × Acceleration
= 400kg × $0.5\,\text{m/s}^2$
= **200N**

## Stopping Distance

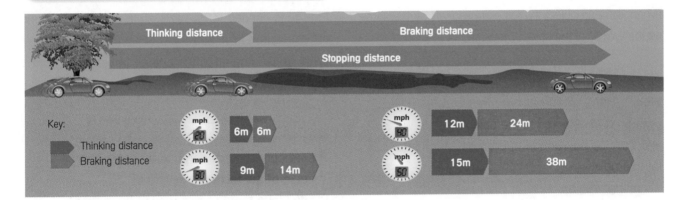

**Stopping distance = Thinking distance + Braking distance**

The stopping distance of a vehicle depends on:
- the thinking distance – the distance travelled by the vehicle from the point the driver realises he needs to brake to when he applies the brakes
- the braking distance – the distance it takes the vehicle to stop once the driver applies the brakes.

The **thinking distance** is **increased** if:
- the vehicle is travelling faster
- the driver is ill, tired or under the influence of alcohol or drugs
- the driver is distracted or isn't concentrating.

The **braking distance** is **increased** if:
- the vehicle is travelling faster
- there is poor weather / bad road conditions, e.g. if it's wet, slippery or icy
- the vehicle is in a poor condition, e.g. worn brakes and tyres or under-inflated tyres.

The thinking distance and braking distance of a vehicle depend on the vehicle's **speed**.

It takes much longer to stop at faster speeds, so road safety regulations advise you to:
- obey the speed limits
- keep your distance from the car in front
- allow extra room between cars (or drive more slowly) in bad weather or poor road conditions.

(HT) The braking distance of a vehicle is increased if:
- the **mass** of the vehicle is **increased** – a loaded vehicle has a greater **kinetic energy**
- the **friction** between the tyres and the road is **decreased** – a wet or greasy road surface reduces the amount of friction between the tyres and the road
- the **braking force** applied is **decreased** – a smaller force is exerted by the brake pads on the wheel discs if the pads are worn
- the vehicle is **travelling faster** – a faster vehicle has greater kinetic energy.

The thinking distance increases linearly:
- Double speed = Double the distance travelled whilst reacting (at constant speed).

The distance follows a squared relationship:
- Double speed = Quadruple the braking distance.
- Triple speed = Multiply the braking distance by 9.

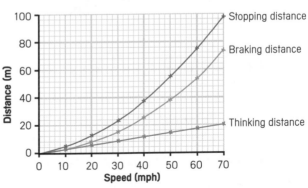

**Thinking, Braking and Stopping Distances**

# P3 Work and Power

## Work

When lifting an object, the force applied will be the same as the weight of the object, measured in newtons:

> **Weight (N) = Mass (kg) × Gravitational field (N/kg)**

**Work** is done whenever a **force** moves an object. Energy is **transferred** to the object. You do work and develop power during everyday activities, for example:

- **lifting** weights
- **climbing** stairs
- **pulling** a rubbish bin
- **pushing** a shopping trolley.

**Energy** is needed to do work. Both energy and work are measured in **joules (J)**.

Work done is equal to the energy transferred (from one form to another).

> **Work done (J) = Energy transferred (J)**

The amount of work done depends on the:

- **size of the force** (in newtons)
- **distance** the object is moved (in metres).

> $$\text{Work done (J)} = \text{Force applied (N)} \times \text{Distance moved in direction of force (m)}$$

## Power

**Power** is a measure of how quickly work is done. Power is measured in **watts (W)**.

Some cars have much higher power ratings than others and may also use more fuel. High fuel consumption is:

- expensive for the driver
- damaging to the environment.

Power, work done and time taken are linked by this formula:

> $$\text{Power (W)} = \frac{\text{Work done (J)}}{\text{Time (s)}}$$

### Example 1

A girl does 2400 joules of work when she runs up a flight of stairs in 8 seconds. Calculate her power.

$$\text{Power} = \frac{\text{Work done}}{\text{Time}} = \frac{2400}{8s} = \textbf{300W}$$

**HT** The **work done** and **power** formulae can be rearranged to work out distance moved or time taken.

### Example 2

A crane does 200 000J of work when it lifts a load of 25 000N. The power of the crane is 50kW.

Calculate the time taken to move the load.

$$\text{Time} = \frac{\text{Work done}}{\text{Power}}$$

*Power must be in watts*

$$= \frac{200\ 000J}{50\ 000W}$$

$$= \textbf{4s}$$

If the speed of an object is known, power can be calculated from:

> **Power (W) = Force (N) × Velocity (m/s)**

## Fuel Consumption

The data shows fuel consumption for two petrol cars. Car 1 has a more **powerful** engine. It travels fewer miles for each gallon of fuel – it uses more petrol per mile than Car 2, so it will be more expensive to run and more harmful to the environment.

| | Engine Size (litres) | Fuel Consumption (mpg) | |
| --- | --- | --- | --- |
| | | Urban | Non-urban |
| Car 1 | 1.6 | 29 | 49 |
| Car 2 | 1.0 | 47 | 71 |

**Key Words**    Transfer • Energy • Joules (J) • Power

## Kinetic Energy

**Kinetic energy** is the energy an object has because of its movement. A ball rolling along the ground, a car travelling along a road and a boy running all have kinetic energy.

The kinetic energy of an object depends on:

- its **mass** (kg)
- its **speed** (m/s).

A **moving** car has kinetic energy.

- If a car moves with a **greater speed** it has **more kinetic energy**.
- If a car has **greater mass** it has **more kinetic energy**.

(HT) Cars with a greater kinetic energy will have a greater braking distance.

You can calculate kinetic energy by using this formula:

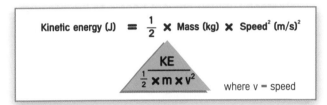

Kinetic energy (J) $= \frac{1}{2} \times$ Mass (kg) $\times$ Speed$^2$ (m/s)$^2$

KE

$\frac{1}{2} \times m \times v^2$          where v = speed

### Example

A car of mass 1000kg is moving at a speed of 10m/s. How much kinetic energy does it have?

Kinetic energy $= \frac{1}{2} \times$ Mass $\times$ Speed$^2$

$= \frac{1}{2} \times 1000$kg $\times (10$m/s$)^2$

$= $ **50 000J** (or **50kJ**)

## Fuel for Vehicles

Most cars rely on petrol or diesel (which come from fossil fuels which are running out) for their energy. But, electricity can also be used, i.e. cars can be driven by battery power or solar power. Cars powered by fossil fuels **pollute** the environment at the **point of use**. Battery-powered cars don't do this, but recharging the batteries uses electricity which is generated in power stations. And power stations **do cause pollution**.

(HT) Biofuels are a possible alternative to fossil fuels. Biofuelled and solar powered vehicles reduce pollution at point of use, which may lead to an overall decrease in $CO_2$ emissions. But they do produce pollution during production.

Car fuel consumption depends on the:

- energy required to increase the kinetic energy
- energy required to work against friction
- driving style, speed and road conditions.

## Frictional Forces

**Frictional** forces, such as **drag**, **friction** and **air resistance**, can act against the movement of the object, slowing it down. These forces can be reduced by:

- changing the shape of the object
- using a lubricant (to make the object slide through the air with less resistance).

The shape of an object can influence its top speed:

- **Badminton shuttlecocks** increase air resistance so they travel slowly.

- **Parachutes** have a larger surface area to increase air resistance.
- **Roof boxes** on cars and open windows increase air resistance.
- **Deflectors** on lorries reduce air resistance.
- **Wedge-shaped** sports cars reduce air resistance.

Greater drag can lead to energy loss and inefficiency (and greater fuel consumption) by vehicles.

## Car Safety Features for Protection

Modern cars have **safety features** that absorb energy in a collision, for example:

- **Seatbelts**, which prevent people in the car from being propelled forwards (though may cause bruising).
- **Air bags**, which cushion the impact for the driver and passengers.
- A **crumple zone**, a part of the car designed to 'crumple' during a collision.
- A **collapsible steering column**, which absorbs energy and breaks to avoid the driver being impaled during an accident.

These features **change shape** during an impact to absorb energy. They protect occupants and reduce the risk of injury during a collision. Seatbelts have to be replaced after a crash because they can be damaged by the forces they experience.

A **safety cage** is a metal cage which strengthens the cabin section of the car. It prevents the vehicle from collapsing when upside down or rolling.

Safety cages don't absorb energy – they remain rigid to prevent the car collapsing on the passengers.

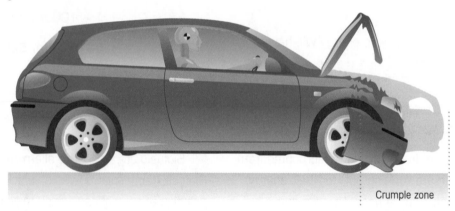

Crumple zone

## Car Safety Features for Prevention

Some car safety features are designed to prevent accidents. Some features make the car itself safer:

- **Anti-lock braking systems** (ABS) prevent the tyres from skidding. This stops the vehicle more quickly and allows the driver to control the steering.
- **Traction control** prevents the car from skidding while accelerating. This helps the driver to get out of a dangerous situation quickly.

Some features help the driver by removing distractions:

- **Electric windows** make it easier for drivers to open and close the windows whilst driving.
- **Paddle shift controls** allow drivers to keep both hands on the steering wheel when changing gear or adjusting the stereo.

**HT** **Anti-lock braking systems** (ABS) prevent the tyres from skidding. They work by pumping the brakes on and off automatically. This increases the area of the tyres that is in contact with the road. **Friction** between the two surfaces is increased, so the braking distance is reduced, and the car is able to stop more quickly.

## Momentum

During a collision a quantity called **momentum** is conserved.

When the car slows down during impact its momentum decreases. As it decreases, the passengers feel a force which can result in injury, e.g. whiplash.

You can calculate momentum using this equation:

> **Momentum = Mass × Velocity**

The force experienced by a passenger during a collision depends upon the rate of changes of momentum. The quicker the change in momentum, the greater the force experienced.

Use the following equation to calculate the force:

> **Force (N) =** $\dfrac{\text{Change in momentum (kg m/s)}}{\text{Time taken (s)}}$

> **Change in momentum = $m_2v_2 - m_1v_1$**
>
> where $m_1$ = initial mass, $m_2$ = final mass, $v_1$ = initial velocity, $v_2$ = final velocity

The quicker the body decelerates, the greater the force felt by the body.

### Example 1
Calculate the force experienced when an 80kg man decelerates from 3m/s to rest (0m/s) in 0.5 seconds.

$$\text{Force} = \frac{(80 \times 0) - (80 \times 3)}{0.5}$$

Force = **480N**

### Example 2
Recalculate the force experienced by the same man, if he now increases the time taken to stop to 2 seconds.

$$\text{Force} = \frac{(80 \times 0) - (80 \times 3)}{2}$$

Force = **120N**

Compare the forces experienced in the collisions in Example 1 and Example 2.

## HT Reducing Stopping Forces

The stopping forces experienced in a collision can be **reduced** by:
- **increasing** the stopping or **collision time**
- **increasing** the stopping or **collision distance**.

All of the standard safety features reduce the stopping forces on the people in the car. This reduces the risk of injury.

Using **Newton's Second Law of Motion**:

| Driving force (f) | = | Mass (kg) | × | Acceleration (m/s²) |
|---|---|---|---|---|
| F | = | m | × | a |

If the collision stopping time is increased (using a crumple zone, for example), the rate of acceleration is decreased so the force is decreased.

## Quick Test

1. List the main features of cars designed to prevent accidents.
2. What feature on a lorry reduces air resistance?
3. HT How does an increase in collision time affect the force felt by the driver?

## Terminal Speed

When a skydiver jumps out of an aeroplane, the speed of his descent can be considered in two separate parts:

- **Before the parachute opens** (when the skydiver is in free-fall).
- **After the parachute opens** (when air resistance is greatly increased).

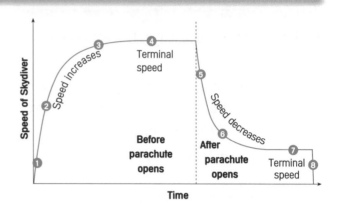

### Before the Parachute Opens

1. When the skydiver jumps, he initially accelerates due to the force of **gravity**.
2. As he falls, he experiences the **frictional force of air resistance** (R) in the opposite direction. At this point, **weight** (W) is **greater than R**, so he continues to accelerate.
3. As his speed increases, so does the air resistance acting on him.
4. Air resistance increases until it's equal to W. The resultant force now acting on him is zero and his falling speed becomes **constant** as forces are balanced. This speed is called the terminal speed.

### After the Parachute Opens

5. When the parachute is opened, unbalanced forces act again because the upward force of R is greatly increased and is bigger than W.
6. The increase in R decreases his speed. As his speed decreases, so does R.
7. R decreases until it's equal to W. The forces acting are once again balanced and, for the second time, he falls at a steady speed, although slower than before. This is a **new terminal speed**.

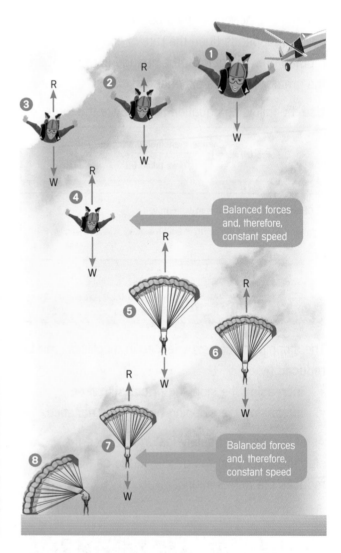

**HT** At **higher speeds**, falling objects experience **more drag**. If you **increase the area** of the object that's facing downwards, **you increase the drag**.

The **terminal speed** occurs when the drag is equal to the weight of the object.

Air resistance • Terminal speed

## HT Terminal Speed

When an object falls at its **terminal speed**:
- the speed isn't changing so the kinetic energy doesn't increase.

- the GPE decreases as the object does work against friction (GPE is transferred into internal or thermal energy of the surrounding air particles by friction).

## Weight and Mass

**Weight** is due to the force of gravity on an object. The **mass** of an object is the amount of matter that it contains. Weight and mass are linked by two related formulae:

Weight (N) = Mass (kg) × Gravitational field strength (N/kg)

Weight (N) = Mass (kg) × Acceleration of free-fall (m/s²)

$$\frac{W}{m \times g}$$

where g = gravitational field strength or acceleration of free-fall

Without air resistance, a falling object near the Earth's surface would have an acceleration of $10m/s^2$. This is known as the **acceleration of free-fall, g**.

The force which causes this acceleration is the weight of the object. The formula is W = mg.

### Example 1
Calculate the weight of a falling stone of mass 0.1kg, if $g = 10m/s^2$.

Weight = Mass × Acceleration of free-fall
= $0.1kg × 10m/s^2$ = **1N**

Near the surface of the Earth the **gravitational field strength**, g, is 10N/kg which means that every 1kg of matter experiences a downwards force, or has a weight, of 10N.

### Example 2
Calculate the weight of a stone of mass 0.1kg on Earth, if g is 10N/kg.

Weight = Mass × Gravitational field strength
= $0.1kg × 10N/kg$ = **1N**

*N.B. Acceleration of free-fall and gravitational field strength are numerically the same, i.e. $10m/s^2$ and 10N/kg. They also both have the same symbol, g.*

## Gravity

Gravitational field strength or acceleration due to gravity:
- is unaffected by atmospheric changes
- varies slightly at different points on the Earth's surface

- will be slightly different on the top of a mountain or down a mineshaft.

## Quick Test

1. Which two forces on a skydiver are equal when he/she is falling at terminal speed?
2. HT When an object falls at its terminal speed, what happens to its kinetic energy?

## Gravitational Potential Energy

The **gravitational potential energy (GPE)** of an object is the energy stored due to:

- its position in the Earth's gravitational field (height)
- its **mass**.

Any object with the **potential** to fall has gravitational potential energy, for example, a person standing on a diving board (before they jump off).

Man A standing on a higher diving board will have **more GPE** than man B standing on a lower diving board (providing they have the same mass). This is because the higher man is further away from the ground.

A heavier man, man C, standing on the **same diving board** as man A will have **more GPE**. This is because the heavier man has a **bigger mass**.

You can calculate GPE using this formula:

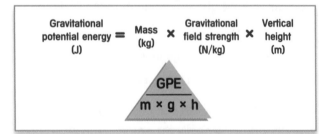

$$\text{Gravitational potential energy (J)} = \text{Mass (kg)} \times \text{Gravitational field strength (N/kg)} \times \text{Vertical height (m)}$$

$$\frac{\text{GPE}}{\text{m} \times \text{g} \times \text{h}}$$

Gravitational field strength, g, is a constant. On Earth it has a value of 10N/kg. This means that every 1kg of matter near the surface of the Earth experiences a downward force of 10N due to gravity.

On planets where the gravitational field strength is higher, the gravitational potential energy is greater.

## HT Examples of GPE

### Example 1

A skier of mass 80kg gets on a ski lift which takes her from a height of 1000m to a height of 3000m. By how much does her gravitational potential energy increase?

= 80kg × 10N/kg × (3000m − 1000m)
= 80kg × 10N/kg × 2000m
**= 1 600 000J (or 1600kJ)**

*N.B. Work done by the ski lift motor has been transferred into gravitational potential energy for the skier.*

### Example 2

A ball is kicked vertically upwards from the ground. Its mass is 0.2kg and it increases its gravitational potential energy by 30J when it reaches the top point in its flight. What height does the ball reach?

Rearrange the formula:

$$\text{Vertical height} = \frac{\text{GPE}}{\text{Mass} \times \text{Gravitational field strength}}$$

$$= \frac{30J}{0.2kg \times 10N/kg} = \textbf{15m}$$

## GPE and Kinetic Energy

When an object falls, it converts **gravitational potential energy (GPE)** into kinetic energy (KE). For example, this happens when:

- a diver jumps off a diving board
- a ball rolls down a hill
- a skydiver jumps out of a plane.

Many theme park rides, for example rollercoasters, also use this transfer of energy.

If the **mass** of a rollercoaster car is **doubled**, the kinetic energy also **doubles**.

If the **speed** of the car is **doubled**, the kinetic energy **quadruples**.

Increasing the **gravitational field strength, g,** will increase the gravitational potential energy. However this couldn't ever happen on Earth as gravitational field strength is **constant**.

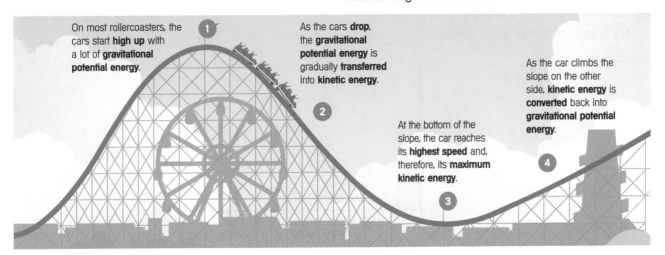

On most rollercoasters, the cars start **high up** with a lot of **gravitational potential energy**.

As the cars **drop**, the **gravitational potential energy** is gradually **transferred** into **kinetic energy**.

At the bottom of the slope, the car reaches its **highest speed** and, therefore, its **maximum kinetic energy**.

As the car climbs the slope on the other side, **kinetic energy** is **converted** back into **gravitational potential energy**.

HT) As an object falls the GPE is converted into kinetic energy. Remember:

$$\text{GPE} = mgh \text{ and KE} = \frac{1}{2}mv^2$$

If all of the GPE is turned into KE:

$$mgh = \frac{1}{2}mv^2$$

The m on each side cancels, leaving:

$$gh = \frac{1}{2}v^2 \text{ or } gh = \frac{v^2}{2}$$

This can be rearranged to calculate the height, h:

$$h = \frac{v^2}{2g}$$

**Example**

A pot of paint falls from the top of some step ladders. Just before it hits the ground it has a velocity of 8m/s. From what height did it fall? (Remember g = 10 m/s²)

$$h = \frac{(8)^2}{2 \times 10}$$

$$= \frac{64}{20}$$

$$= 3.2 \text{ m}$$

## Quick Test

1. What happens to the size of the kinetic energy of an object if its speed is doubled?
2. HT) What is the value of the gravitational field strength on Earth?
3. HT) What is the unit of GPE?

# P3 Exam Practice Questions

1 a) What two things do you need to know in order to calculate the acceleration of an object? **[2]**

b) Draw lines between the boxes to match each statement with its meaning on a speed–time graph.

| | |
|---|---|
| Straight line with a positive gradient | Constant speed |
| Straight line with a negative gradient | Deceleration |
| Horizontal straight line | Acceleration |

**[2]**

2 Tom has just started taking driving lessons and is interested in thinking, braking and stopping distances. He is looking at the graph below.

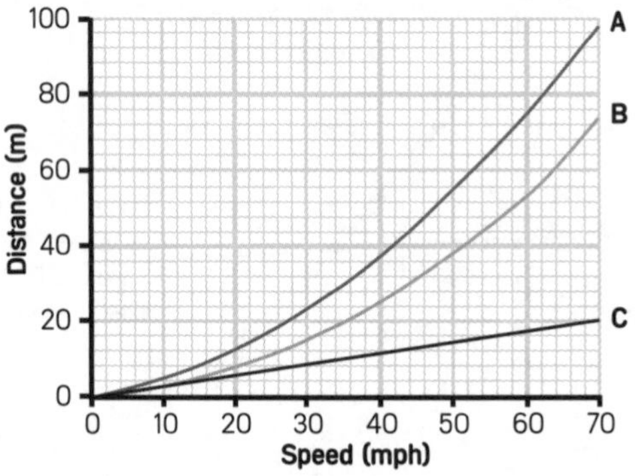

a) Which of the graph lines, A, B or C represents the thinking distance? **[1]**

b) How long would the braking distance be if a vehicle was travelling at 45mph? **[1]**

c) Write about the factors which increase thinking distance of a driver. **[4]**

3 Kinetic energy is the energy an object has because of its movement.

a) What two things does the kinetic energy of an object depend on? **[1]**

b) A 2000kg van is travelling at 20m/s. Calculate its kinetic energy. **[2]**

4 Describe three safety features of modern cars that protect the occupants in the event of a collision. **[3]**

........................................................................................................................................

........................................................................................................................................

5 Put the following sentences into the correct order by numbering them **1** to **4**. **[3]**

A   The skydiver reaches a very high terminal speed where air resistance is equal to his weight. ☐

B   The skydiver slows down to reach a lower terminal speed. ☐

C   As the skydiver falls, his speed increases because his weight is greater than air resistance. ☐

D   When he opens his parachute, the air resistance becomes greater than his weight. ☐

6 Calculate the height of a 160g cricket ball if it has 30J of gravitational potential energy. **[2]**

........................................................................................................................................

........................................................................................................................................

7 **a)** William has a car of mass 1100kg. He slows down from 50 mph (22.3m/s) to 30 mph     **[2]**
(13.4m/s) as he drives into a village. Calculate the change in momentum of the car.

........................................................................................................................................

HT

**b)** As William drives, a girl runs into the road and he has to do an emergency stop. He reduces
his speed from 13.4m/s to rest in 2.2s.

**i)**   Calculate the change in momentum of the car. **[2]**

........................................................................................................................................

**ii)**  What force must the brakes apply to stop the car in this time? **[2]**

........................................................................................................................................

8 A new theme park ride lifts its occupants vertically. It then drops vertically downwards under the
influence of gravity.     **[3]**
Assuming there is no energy loss (as heat or sound), calculate the maximum velocity reached after
the ride has dropped 30m. (Use g = 10m/s$^2$)

........................................................................................................................................

# P4 Sparks

## Generating Static Electricity

An insulating material can become electrically **charged** if it's rubbed with another insulating material. **Electrons** (which have a negative charge) transfer from one material to the other, leaving:

- one material with a **positive** charge
- one material with a **negative** charge.

You can generate **static electricity** by rubbing a balloon, comb or strip of plastic against a jumper. The electrically charged object will attract very small objects, e.g. pieces of paper or cork.

**Dusting brushes** can be charged so that they attract dust when they pass over the brush.

**Synthetic clothing** can become charged due to **friction** between the clothing and the person's body when the clothes are put on. When the clothing is removed from the body, static sparks are sometimes produced.

The balloon is rubbed against the jumper

Paper then clings to the balloon

## Discharging Static Electricity

A **charged object** can be **discharged** (i.e. have the excess charge removed) by **earthing** it. When an object discharges, electrons are transferred from the charged object to earth.

If you become charged and then earthed, you could get an **electrostatic shock**.

For example, you can become charged by friction between the soles of your feet and the floor if you're walking on an insulator such as carpet or vinyl. If you then touch a **water pipe**, e.g. a radiator, the charge is earthed and discharge occurs, giving you a shock.

## Problems of Static Electricity

In some situations, static electricity can be a **nuisance**.

For example, static can cause:

- dirt and dust to be attracted to insulating materials, e.g. television screens and computer monitors
- some materials to cling to your skin.

In other situations, static electricity can be very **dangerous**:

- Flour mills and petrochemical factories have atmospheres that can contain extremely flammable gases (or vapours), or high concentrations of oxygen. A discharge of static electricity (i.e. a spark) can lead to an explosion.
- Static is dangerous in any situation where large amounts could flow through your body to earth, for example, lightning.

**Key Words**            **Electron • Static electricity • Friction • Earthed**

## Repulsion and Attraction

Two insulating materials with the **same charge** will **repel** each other. For example, if a **positively charged** Perspex rod is held near to a suspended **positively charged** Perspex rod, the suspended rod will be **repelled**. The same thing would happen if both rods had a negative charge.

Two insulating materials with **different charges** will **attract** each other. For example, if a **negatively charged** ebonite rod is held near to a suspended **positively charged** Perspex rod, the suspended rod will be **attracted** to the ebonite rod. This would also happen if the charges were the other way round.

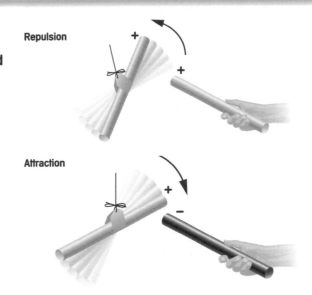

Repulsion

Attraction

## HT Charging Up Objects

Electric or static charge builds up when **electrons** (negatively charged) are rubbed off one material onto another.

- The material that **receives** the electrons becomes **negatively charged** due to an **excess of electrons**.
- The material **giving up the** electrons becomes **positively charged** due to a **loss of electrons.**

A Perspex rod rubbed with a cloth gives up electrons and becomes positively charged. The cloth receives the electrons and becomes negatively charged.

An ebonite rod rubbed with fur receives electrons and becomes negatively charged. The fur gives up electrons and becomes positively charged.

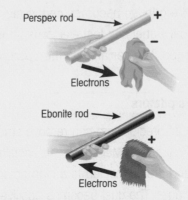

Perspex rod

Electrons

Ebonite rod

Electrons

Atoms and molecules that have become charged are called **ions**.
- If they have an excess of electrons they are **negative ions**.
- If they have lost electrons they are **positive ions**.

## Reducing the Danger

The chance of receiving an electric shock can be **reduced** by:
- making sure appliances are correctly earthed
- using insulation mats effectively
- wearing shoes with insulating soles.

Lorries that contain inflammable gases, liquids or powders need to be earthed before unloading, as

friction can cause a build-up of charge. This charge could lead to a spark, which could then ignite the flammable substance.

Anti-static sprays, liquids and cloths help to reduce the problems of static electricity by preventing the transfer of charge from one insulator to another. If there is no build-up of charge, there can't be any discharge.

# P4 Uses of Electrostatics

## Using Static in Everyday Life

**Static electricity** is used in many ways, including spray painting, smoke precipitators and defibrillators.

### Quick Test

1. Name the two types of electric charge.
2. What is the job of a defibrillator?
3. (HT) How does a material become positively charged?

### Spray Painting

The paint particles are given a negative charge so that they repel each other, forming a fine spray. This ensures that the paint is applied evenly. The panel to be sprayed is positively charged so it attracts the negatively charged paint. This means that less paint is wasted and even the back and sides of the object, in the shadow of the spray, receive a coat of paint.

In a similar way, electrostatics can be used in crop-spraying.

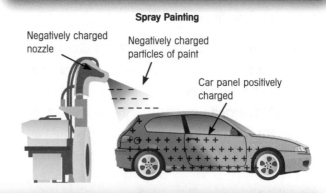

**Spray Painting**

Negatively charged nozzle

Negatively charged particles of paint

Car panel positively charged

(HT) The paint gains electrons as it passes through the nozzle of the gun, so becomes negatively charged. The car panel has lost electrons so is left positively charged. The car attracts the oppositely charged paint. As the paint sticks to the car, the charges cancel so the car becomes neutrally charged and no more paint is attracted. The car receives an even coat of paint.

### Smoke Precipitators

Electrostatic dust precipitators can remove smoke particles from chimneys. Metal grids are installed in the chimney and are connected to a high potential difference (voltage). The dust becomes positively charged as it passes the grid, inducing a positive charge on the dust. The dust particles are attracted to the negative charged plates, where they form large particles that fall back down the chimney when they are heavy enough, or if the plates are stuck.

(HT) The dust particles become charged when they lose electrons.

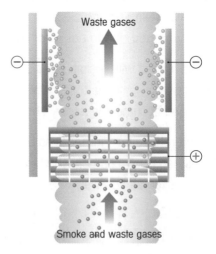

**Smoke Precipitator**

Waste gases

Smoke and waste gases

### Defibrillators

Electricity can be used to start the heart when it has stopped. Two paddles are charged and are put in good electrical contact with the patient's chest using gel. Taking care not to shock the operator, charge is then passed through the patient to make the heart contract.

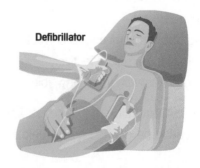

**Defibrillator**

## Circuits

A **circuit** is a complete loop that allows an **electrical current** to flow. **Electrons** flow around the circuit from the **negative electrode** of the power source to the **positive electrode**. But this was only discovered recently so circuit diagrams are drawn showing the current flowing from **the positive to the negative** electrode.

## Fixed and Variable Resistors

**Resistance** is a measure of how hard it is to get a current through a **component** in a circuit at a particular **voltage** (potential difference). Resistance is measured in **ohms** ($\Omega$).

The current through a circuit can be controlled by varying the resistance. There are two types of resistor:

- **A fixed resistor** has **constant** resistance. The bigger the resistance, the smaller the current that flows for a particular voltage.
- **A variable resistor** (or rheostat) has a **changeable** resistance.

The resistance of the rheostat can be changed by moving the slider, changing the length of wire between the contacts.

- Long wire = high resistance, low current.
- Short wire = low resistance, large current.

**Variable Resistors**

High resistance
Sliding the contrast

Low resistance

## Current, Voltage and Resistance

For a **given resistor**, **current increases** as **voltage increases** (and vice versa). For a **fixed voltage**, **current decreases** as **resistance increases** (and vice versa).

Current, voltage and resistance are related by this formula:

$$\text{Resistance } (\Omega) = \frac{\text{Voltage (V)}}{\text{Current (A)}}$$

where I is the current

$$\frac{V}{R \times I}$$

**Example 1**

Calculate the resistance of the lamp in the circuit:

$$\text{Resistance} = \frac{\text{Voltage}}{\text{Current}} = \frac{3V}{0.2A} = 15\Omega$$

**Example 2**

Calculate the reading on the ammeter in this circuit if the bulb has a resistance of 20 ohms.

$$\text{Current} = \frac{\text{Voltage}}{\text{Resistance}} = \frac{6V}{20\Omega} = \textbf{0.3A}$$

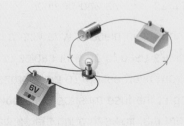

# P4 Safe Electricals

## Live, Neutral and Earth Wires

Electrical appliances are connected to mains electricity by a cable and 3-pin plug. Most cables and plugs contain three wires:

- **Live wire** (brown) – carries current to the appliance at a high voltage (230V).
- **Neutral wire** (blue) – completes the circuit and carries current away from the appliance.
- **Earth wire** (green and yellow) – safety wire that stops the appliance becoming live.

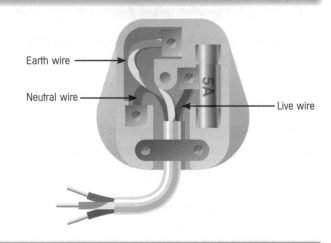

Earth wire

Neutral wire

5A

Live wire

## Double Insulation

All appliances with outer metal cases (**conductors**) have an **earth wire**, so they are **earthed**. An earthed conductor can't become live.

Appliances with **cases made of insulators** don't have an earth wire (although they still have a **fuse**). They are **double insulated** so they can't become live.

## (HT) Earthing

Electrical appliances with outer metal cases are earthed in order to protect the appliance and the user. The earth wire and fuse work together.

1. A fault in the appliance causes the casing to become live.
2. The circuit **short-circuits** (i.e. the path of the flow of charge changes) because the earth wire offers less resistance.
3. The fuse wire melts.
4. The circuit is broken.
5. The appliance and the user are protected.

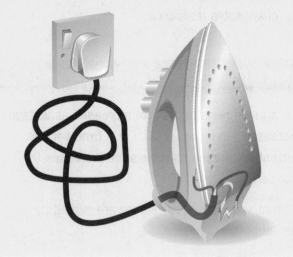

## Fuses and Circuit Breakers

Fuses and **circuit breakers** are **safety devices** designed to break a circuit if a fault occurs. This can prevent fires, injuries and deaths.

A **fuse** is a short, thin piece of wire with a low melting point. It's used to prevent cables or appliances from overheating. To work properly, the current rating of the fuse must be **just above** the normal current that flows through the appliance.

1. A fault causes the current in the appliance to exceed the current rating of the fuse.
2. The fuse wire gets hot and melts or breaks.
3. The circuit is broken so the current is unable to flow.
4. The appliance and user are protected.

A **circuit breaker** acts in a similar way to a fuse, but it can be easily **reset** rather than replaced.

Conductor • Insulator • Fuse • Circuit breaker

## Power

The power rating of a device tells you how quickly electrical energy is being changed (transferred) into another form within that device. Power is measured in Watts (W). For example, a 2400W hairdryer changes electrical energy into heat and **kinetic energy** (as well as some sound) at a rate of 2400 joules each second.

| Power (W) | = | Current (A) | × | Voltage (V) |

(HT) Calculate the current which flows in a 2400W hairdryer, when it is plugged in to the 230V mains supply.

$$I = \frac{P}{V}$$

$$= \frac{2400W}{230V}$$

$$= \textbf{10.4 Amps}$$

The plug should be fitted with a 13A fuse.

## (HT) Example of a Fuse in Action

1. If the current flowing through an appliance is **below** the **current rating** of the fuse, the appliance will work properly.
2. But, if a fault occurs inside the appliance, the live wire will make contact with the neutral wire. The current flowing would then be **higher** than the **current rating** of the fuse due to lower resistance.
3. This causes the fuse wire to get hotter and hotter until it melts and breaks the circuit. The current is unable to flow so there is no danger of the flex overheating (resulting in a fire). Further damage to the appliance, or injury to the user, is prevented.

Fuses and circuit breakers prevent:
- injury and death as they stop appliances from becoming 'live'
- fires as they stop cables and flexes from overheating
- damage to the components of an appliance because they break the circuit if a higher than normal current flows through the appliance.

1

2 As the current increases, the fuse gets hotter

Insulators wear away and wires touch

3

The fuse melts and breaks the circuit

## Quick Test

1. State the equation used to calculate resistance.
2. Name the wires in a three-pin plug and give the colour of each.
3. What happens to a fuse when too much current flows through it?
4. (HT) Fuses and circuit breakers are used to prevent what three things?

**Key Words**        Kinetic energy

# P4 Ultrasound

## Ultrasound

**Ultrasound** is sound waves with frequencies above the upper limit of the human hearing range (i.e. above about 20 000 hertz (Hz)).

Ultrasound travels in a **longitudinal wave**. This can be demonstrated using a slinky spring.

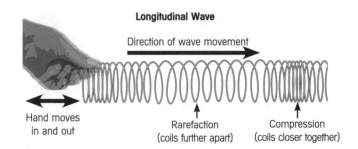

**Longitudinal Wave**

Direction of wave movement

Hand moves in and out

Rarefaction (coils further apart)

Compression (coils closer together)

### Key Features of Waves

The key features of waves are:
- **Rarefaction** – area of low pressure.
- **Compression** – area of high pressure.
- **Wavelength** – the distance between corresponding points on two successive disturbances.
- **Frequency** – the number of waves produced (or that pass a particular point) in 1 second.

(HT) • **Amplitude** – the maximum disturbance caused by a wave.

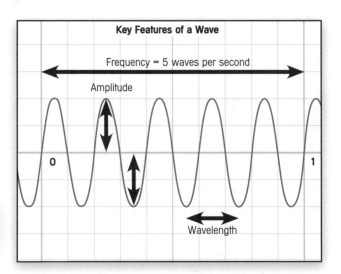

**Key Features of a Wave**

Frequency = 5 waves per second

Amplitude

0

1

Wavelength

## Applications of Ultrasound

Ultrasound can be used in **medicine**. **Scanning** the body with ultrasound waves can build up a picture of the body's organs, including the heart, lungs and liver.

Ultrasound waves can **break down kidney stones** so they can be removed from the body naturally. This avoids the need for painful surgery.

(HT) Ultrasonic waves cause the kidney stones to vibrate. The stones break up, are dispersed, and can then be passed out of the body in urine.

Ultrasound can be used:
- to measure the **speed of blood flow**
- to detect **gallstones** and **tumours**
- for **pre-natal scanning** because there is less risk to mother or baby than using X-rays.

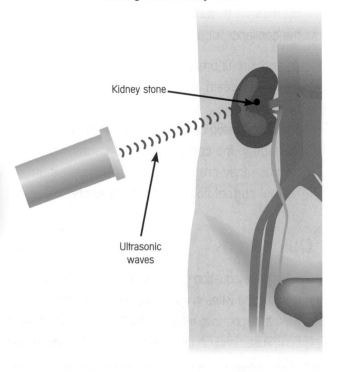

**Breaking Down a Kidney Stone**

Kidney stone

Ultrasonic waves

Ultrasound • Longitudinal wave • Rarefaction • Compression • Wavelength • Frequency

## HT More on Ultrasound

Ultrasound waves are **partially reflected** at a **boundary** as they pass from one medium or substance into another. The **time taken** for these **reflections** to be **detected** can be used to calculate the depth of the reflecting surface. The reflected waves are usually processed to produce a visual image on a screen.

Ultrasound has two main advantages over X-ray imaging:
- It's able to produce images of soft tissue.
- It doesn't damage living cells.

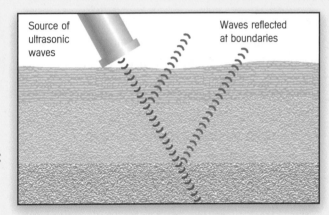

Source of ultrasonic waves

Waves reflected at boundaries

## Particle Motion in Waves

All waves **transfer energy** from one point to another **without** transferring any **particles of matter**. In the following diagrams, each coil of the slinky spring represents one particle. There are two types of wave – **longitudinal** and **transverse**.

| Longitudinal Waves | Transverse Waves |
|---|---|
| Each particle moves backwards and forwards about its normal position in the same plane as the direction of wave movement. | Each particle moves up and down about its normal position at 90° to the direction of the wave movement. |
| Direction of energy transfer<br><br>Hand moves in and out | Direction of energy transfer<br><br>Hand moves up and down |
| | |
| | |

## Quick Test

1. Write a definition for frequency.
2. State two medical uses of ultrasound.
3. What are the advantages of using ultrasound instead of X-rays?

# P4 What is Radioactivity?

## Radioactivity

Radioactive **materials** give out nuclear radiation from the nucleus of each of their atoms. The atoms are **unstable** and **decay naturally**.

During this decay, radiation can be given out in the form of alpha, beta and gamma rays:
- An **alpha particle** is a **helium** nucleus.
- A **beta particle** is a fast-moving **electron**.
- Gamma is an electromagnetic wave (energy).

Radiation is measured by the **number of nuclear decays emitted per second**. This number decreases with time.

Ionisation occurs when an uncharged (neutral) atom gains or loses electrons.

**HT** Alpha radiation is highly ionising because it's missing two electrons (it has a 2+ electric charge). It attracts electrons away from atoms it passes, leaving them positively charged.

## **HT** Alpha Emission

During alpha emission, the atom decays by ejecting an **alpha particle** (a helium nucleus made up of two protons and two neutrons) from the nucleus.

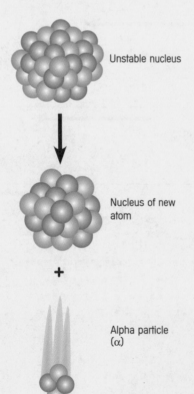

Unstable nucleus

Nucleus of new atom

+

Alpha particle
($\alpha$)

The nucleus of the new atom formed differs from the original one in a number of ways:
- It is a different element.
- It has two fewer protons and two fewer neutrons.
- The atomic number has decreased by two.
- The mass number has decreased by four.

**Example** – alpha decay of radium-226 into radon-222:

$$^{226}_{88}\text{Ra} \longrightarrow ^{222}_{86}\text{Rn} + ^{4}_{2}\alpha$$

*N.B. The mass numbers (at the top) and the atomic numbers (at the bottom) balance on both sides.*

## Beta Emission

During beta emission, the atom decays by changing a neutron into a **proton** and an **electron**. The high-energy electron ejected from the nucleus is a **beta particle**.

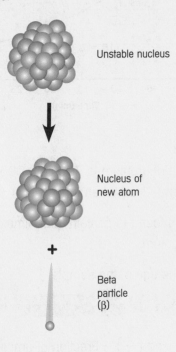

Unstable nucleus

Nucleus of new atom

+

Beta particle (β)

The nucleus of the new atom formed differs from the original one in a number of ways:

- It has one more proton and one less neutron.
- The atomic number has increased by one.
- The mass number remains the same.

**Example** – Beta decay of iodine-131 into xenon-131:

$$^{131}_{53}I \longrightarrow \, ^{131}_{54}Xe \, + \, ^{0}_{-1}\beta$$

N.B. The mass numbers (at the top) and the atomic numbers (at the bottom) balance on both sides.

## Half-life

**Half-life** is the time it takes for half the undecayed nuclei in a radioactive substance to decay.

If the substance has a very **long half-life** then it remains **active** for a very **long time**.

Igneous rocks can contain uranium atoms which decay to produce stable atoms of lead. It's possible to date rocks by:

- measuring the proportion of uranium and lead in the rock
- knowing the half-life of uranium.

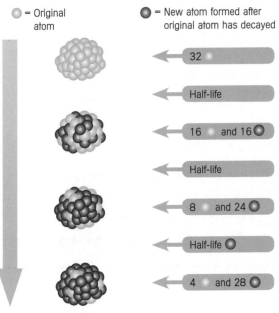

**Atoms in a Sample of Radioactive Substance**

○ = Original atom  ● = New atom formed after original atom has decayed

32 ○

Half-life

16 ○ and 16 ●

Half-life

8 ○ and 24 ●

Half-life ●

4 ○ and 28 ●

N.B. This is a collection of atoms, not a nucleus.

# P4 What is Radioactivity?

## Calculations Involving Half-life

Half-life can be calculated using a table or a graph.

### Example 1

The table shows the activity of a radioactive substance against time.

| Time (min) | Activity (Bq) |
|------------|---------------|
| 0 | 200 |
| 5 | 160 |
| 10 | 124 |
| 15 | 100 |
| 20 | 80 |
| 25 | 62 |
| 30 | 50 |

Calculate the half-life of the substance by:

**a)** using a table

**b)** drawing a graph.

**a)** Find an average by choosing three pairs of points between which the activity has halved.

| Activity | Time | Half-Life |
|----------|------|-----------|
| 200 → 100 | 0 → 15 | 15 min |
| 160 → 80 | 5 → 20 | 15 min |
| 100 → 50 | 15 → 30 | 15 min |

The half-life is **15 minutes**.

**b)**

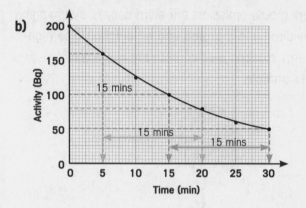

### Example 2

The half-life of uranium is 700 000 000 years. Uranium forms lead when it decays.

A sample is found to contain three times as much lead as uranium.

Calculate the age of the sample.

> Fraction of lead present is $\frac{3}{4}$. Fraction of uranium present is $\frac{1}{4}$.

Fraction of lead $\left(\frac{3}{4}\right)$ + Fraction of uranium $\left(\frac{1}{4}\right)$ = Original amount of uranium $(1)$.

> Work out the number of decays it takes to get $\frac{1}{4}$.

1 — half-life → $\frac{1}{2}$ — half-life → $\frac{1}{4}$     ← 2 half-lives

Age of rock = 2 × half-life

= 2 × 700 000 000 years

= **1 400 000 000 years**

## Quick Test

1. How is radiation measured?
2. A substance with a very long half-life remains active for a very short time. True or false?
3. Describe an alpha particle.
4. **HT** During beta emission, the atom decays by changing a neutron into what?

## Background Radiation

Background **radiation** occurs naturally in our environment and is all around us. **Most** background radiation is released by:

- radioactive substances in soil and rocks
- **cosmic rays** from outer space.

Some background radiation comes from man-made sources and waste products. Industry and hospitals both contribute to background radiation levels, but this is only a small percentage of the total background radiation.

## Tracers

**Radioisotopes** are used as **tracers** in industry and hospitals. In industry, tracers are used to:

- track the dispersal of waste
- find leaks and blockages in underground pipes
- find the routes of underground pipes.

A radioactive material that emits gamma rays is put into the pipe. (Gamma is used because

it can penetrate through the soil to the surface.) The progress of the material is then tracked by a detector above ground. If there is a:

- **leak** – the radioactive material will **escape** and be detected at the surface
- **blockage** – the radioactive material will **stop flowing** so it can't be detected after this point.

## Smoke Detectors

Most smoke detectors contain **Americium-241**, an **alpha emitter**. Emitted particles cause air particles to **ionise**, and the ions formed are attracted to the oppositely charged electrodes. This results in a flow of electric current. This is what happens when smoke enters the space between the two electrodes:

1 The alpha particles are absorbed by the smoke particles.

2 Less **ionisation** takes place.

3 A smaller current than normal now flows, and the alarm sounds.

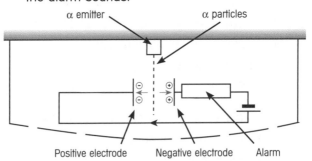

## Carbon Dating

A small amount of the carbon in our atmosphere and the bodies of animals and plants is radioactive Carbon-14.

(HT) The activity of radioactive carbon can be used to find the approximate age of a once-living material. The amount of radioactive Carbon-14 in the atmosphere has remained unchanged for thousands of years. A dead object doesn't exchange gases with the air as living matter does. As the Carbon-14

**Measurements** from **radioactive carbon** can be used to **date** old, once-living materials, such as wood.

in the dead object **decays**, it is not replaced so the radioactivity of the sample **decreases**.

So, the dead object will have a different radioactivity to living matter. The **ratio** of these two activities can be used to find a fairly accurate approximate age for the object within known limits (approximately 50 years).

## Radiation

X-rays and gamma rays are **electromagnetic waves** with similar **wavelengths** but they are produced in different ways.

X-rays and nuclear **radiation** (i.e. gamma and beta radiation) can be used in medicine.

X-rays can be used to build up a picture of the inside of a patient's body. The person in a hospital who takes X-rays and uses radiation is called a **radiographer**.

Medical radioisotopes are produced by placing materials in a nuclear reactor. They become radioactive when they absorb extra neutrons.

(HT) X-rays are made by firing high-speed **electrons** at metal targets. X-rays are easier to control than gamma rays.

Gamma rays **damage cells**, so they can be used to **treat cancer**.

Gamma (and sometimes beta) can pass through the skin (unlike alpha), so can be used as medical **tracers** (i.e. to track the progress of a substance through a patient's system). They are only inside the body for a short time to avoid damage to healthy tissue.

Gamma rays can also be used to **sterilise medical equipment** because they kill germs and bacteria.

After alpha or beta decay, a nucleus sometimes contains surplus energy. It emits this as gamma radiation, which is very high frequency electromagnetic radiation.

## Treating Cancer

Gamma rays can be used to treat cancer:
1. A wide beam of **gamma rays** from a source outside the body is focused on the tumour.
2. The beam is rotated around the outside of the body with the tumour at the centre.
3. This concentrates the gamma rays on the tumour, but minimises damage to the rest of the body.

Gamma radiation treatment can destroy cancer cells without the need for surgery, but it may damage healthy cells and cause sickness.

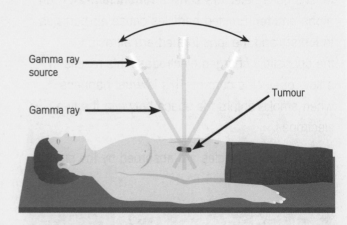

Gamma ray source

Gamma ray

Tumour

## Tracers

**Tracers** are small amounts of radioactive materials (with a short half-life) which are swallowed or injected into a patient. The tracer spreads through the body, whilst its progress is followed using an external radiation detector (a gamma camera).

For example, the thyroid gland in the neck affects the body's metabolic rate. It absorbs iodine, so a patient can be given a tracer which contains radioactive iodine-131. A detector follows the progress of a tracer. You can tell how well the gland is working by measuring the amount of iodine it absorbs.

N.B. The radioactive material **must** emit either gamma or beta radiation, because they both pass through skin so they can be detected outside the body.

## Producing Electricity

Power stations use **energy sources** to produce electricity.

**Conventional** power stations **burn** fossil fuels (coal, oil and gas). This produces heat which boils water and creates **steam**.

**Nuclear** power stations use **uranium**. A nuclear reaction takes place which produces the heat required to make **steam**. The nuclear reaction is called **fission**.

Both power stations then **use the steam** to drive turbines, which turn generators and produce electricity.

**Nuclear Reactor**

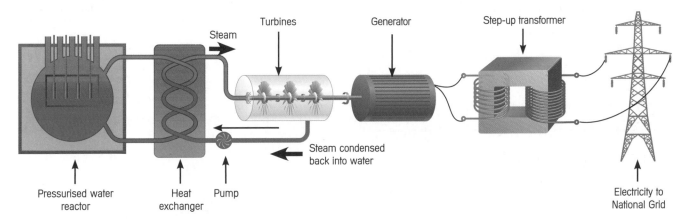

Steam · Turbines · Generator · Step-up transformer

Pressurised water reactor · Heat exchanger · Pump · Steam condensed back into water · Electricity to National Grid

## Fission

**Nuclear fission** is the process by which heat energy is released when a radioactive nucleus (i.e. uranium) **splits**. This heat energy can be used in a nuclear reactor.

When a uranium nucleus absorbs an extra neutron it splits, releasing energy and more neutrons. These neutrons can then cause further uranium nuclei to split. This is called a **chain reaction**.

Nuclear fission produces radioactive waste, which can be dangerous.

A nuclear bomb is a chain reaction that has gone out of control. It results in one powerful release of energy.

# P4 Fission and Fusion

## Fusion

**Nuclear fusion** is the process by which heat energy is released when nuclei join (**fuse**) together. Fusion happens easily in stars, but is not yet a practical energy resource on Earth.

## HT Small Scale Nuclear Fission

1. The uranium atom is hit with a neutron.
2. The nucleus splits into two smaller nuclei (e.g. barium and krypton).
3. Energy and new neutrons are released.
4. The new atoms formed (barium and krypton), are themselves radioactive.

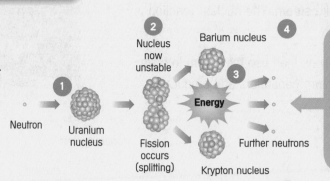

Neutron

Uranium nucleus

Nucleus now unstable

Fission occurs (splitting)

Barium nucleus

Energy

Krypton nucleus

Further neutrons

If more than one neutron is released when the uranium nucleus splits, these neutrons can cause further uranium nuclei to split. This is called a **chain reaction**.

## Large Scale Nuclear Fission

Scientists stop nuclear reactions getting out of control by placing **control rods** in the reactor.

The rods absorb some of the neutrons (preventing further fissions).

They can be lowered or raised to control the number of neutrons available for fission, which allows the process to keep operating safely.

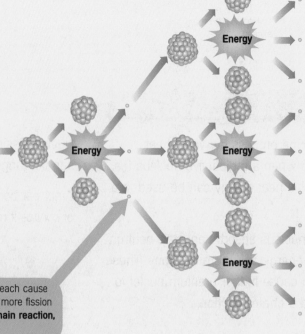

Energy

The energy is released in the form of heat. Each fission reaction only produces a tiny amount of energy, but there are billions and billions of reactions every second.

The new neutrons produced can each cause further uranium nuclei to split, so more fission reactions are created. This is a **chain reaction**, so it carries on and on and on.

## Nuclear Fusion

When two nuclei **join** (fuse) together a large amount of **heat energy is released**. This can only happen at **extremely** high temperatures.

It is very difficult to manage these high temperatures, so **nuclear fusion** is **not** yet a possible energy source on Earth.

An example of a fusion reaction is when two hydrogen nuclei join to form a helium nucleus. This takes place in stars and fusion bombs (also called H-bombs or hydrogen bombs).

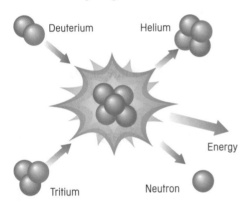

Deuterium　　Helium

Energy

Tritium　　Neutron

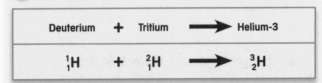

(HT) Different isotopes of hydrogen can undergo fusion:

| Deuterium | + | Tritium | ⟶ | Helium-3 |
|---|---|---|---|---|
| $^{1}_{1}H$ | + | $^{2}_{1}H$ | ⟶ | $^{3}_{2}H$ |

In **stars**, fusion happens very easily. On Earth, scientists have **not yet** been able to produce the **extremely high temperatures and pressures** needed to keep a fusion reaction going long enough for practical power generation.

In a fusion bomb the initial high temperatures needed are produced by a fission reaction.

### Quick Test

1. What are the three types of nuclear radiation?
2. Which type of radiation is used to treat cancer?
3. Which type of radiation releases high energy electrons?

## Cold Fusion

Ordinarily, fusion reactions require extremely high temperatures and pressures for two nuclei to fuse (join) together. When two nuclei fuse, energy is released. For decades, scientists have been attempting to reproduce fusion reactions under controlled conditions in laboratories. If the reaction can be controlled then the energy released could be harnessed and used as an alternative energy source, replacing fossil fuels. **Cold fusion** refers to a fusion reaction that occurs at room temperature.

In 1989 **Martin Fleischmann** and **Stanley Pons** claimed to have achieved a cold fusion reaction. When a new discovery is made, it's important to **share data** with other scientists. Scientists from across the world are then able to try to **replicate** the experiment. They must check that the experiment can be repeated and that the same

data can be produced. This shows that the discovery is genuine (i.e. it hasn't been invented, e.g. for publicity) and it doesn't show **anomalous results** (errors). It's only when experiments are repeated, and matching data collected (over and over again) that a new theory can be accepted. The data produced by Fleischmann and Pons couldn't be replicated.

(HT) Despite over 20 years of research since Fleischmann and Pons' claims, nobody has been able to successfully reproduce their experiment. Until data from cold fusion experiments can be gathered in repeated experiments and the reaction sustained to produce large quantities of energy, cold fusion isn't a realistic method of energy production.

**1 a)** *The build up of charge is due to the transfer of positive electrons. Is this statement **true** or **false**?* **[1]**
Explain your answer.

........................................................................................................................................................................

........................................................................................................................................................................

**b)** Suggest two uses of electrostatics. **[2]**

........................................................................................................................................................................

**2 a)** Draw lines between the boxes to link each type of wire to its correct colour. **[2]**

| Neutral | | Green and yellow |
|---------|---|------------------|
| Earth | | Brown |
| Live | | Blue |

**b)** *Double insulated appliances require neither a fuse nor an earth wire. Is this statement **true** or **false**?* **[1]**
Explain your answer. ..............................................................................................................................

**3 a)** A 12V supply causes a current of 0.3A to flow through a bulb. Calculate the resistance. **[2]**

........................................................................................................................................................................

**b)** The bulb is replaced by one with a resistance of 80Ω. What is the new current in the circuit? **[2]**

........................................................................................................................................................................

**4** Describe nuclear fusion and explain why it is not yet a possible energy resource on Earth. **[6]**

🖉 *The quality of your written communication will be assessed in your answer to this question.*

........................................................................................................................................................................

........................................................................................................................................................................

........................................................................................................................................................................

........................................................................................................................................................................

........................................................................................................................................................................

........................................................................................................................................................................

........................................................................................................................................................................

........................................................................................................................................................................

5 The explosion at the Chernobyl Nuclear Reactor released a large cloud of radioactive gas into the atmosphere, which spread over Europe. The gas contained caesium-137 (with a half-life of 30 years) and iodine-131. The following table shows measurements of the count rate from a small sample of iodine-131.

| Time (Days) | 0 | 4 | 8 | 12 |
|---|---|---|---|---|
| Count Rate (Bq) | 320 | 230 | 160 | 115 |

a) Using the data in the table, work out the half-life of iodine-131.                    [1]

b) Four months after the explosion, scientists were less concerned about the health risks from the iodine but were still worried about the effects from the caesium-137. Do you think they were right to be concerned? Explain your answer.                    [3]

# Answers

## Biology

### B3 Living and Growing

**Quick Test Answers**

**Page 7**
1. Mitochondria.
2. A–T and C–G

**Page 12**
1. glucose + oxygen → carbon dioxide + water + energy
2. Lactic acid
3. Sex cells (egg and sperm).
4. Sex organs (e.g. ovaries and testes).
5. Red cells, white cells, platelets, plasma.
6. Take blood from the heart to the lungs to pick up oxygen.

**Page 16**
1. Selective breeding.
2. Changing a person's genes in an attempt to cure a genetic disorder.
3. The production of human insulin by genetically engineered bacteria.

**Page 19**
1. Twins
2. Dolly the sheep.
3. Mass production of animals with desirable characteristics; Producing lots of animals which produce a human product; Producing human embryos to supply stem cells for therapy.

**Answers to Exam Practice Questions**
1. a) 1 = Vena cava; 2 = Pulmonary artery; 3 = Aorta; 4 = Pulmonary vein
   b) To prevent backflow / let blood flow in the right direction.
2. a) 28
   b) 40
   c) It is a similar number. Humans have 46 chromosomes, mice have 40.

3. a)
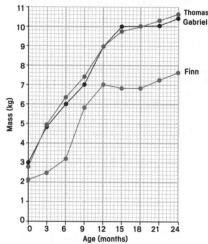
   b) Between 0 and 3 months
   c) He is healthy/No growth problems.
4. a) An identical copy of an organism.
   b) Religious or ethical suggestion, unnatural / against God / against their beliefs; Disease risk linked to transplanted organs; Money could be better spent on new medicines; Reduces variation; Possible abnormalities; Premature ageing. **[Any two for 2]**
   c) Identical twins.
   d) Nucleus removed from egg (cell) of sheep (A) **[1]**
   Nucleus from body cell / sheep B placed in egg (cell) **[1]**
   Egg (cell) implanted / put into surrogate sheep. **[1]**
   e) B because the DNA / genes / chromosomes came from sheep B.
5. a) 4
   b) T G C A

### B4 It's a Green World

**Quick Test Answers**

**Page 27**
1. Pooters, sweepnets, pitfall traps, quadrats.
2. As a kite diagram.
3. Starch
4. More light, more carbon dioxide, higher temperature.

**Page 31**
1. Through the stomata.
2. On the underside of leaves.
3. Root cells.
4. It is the water pressure inside cells acting against the inelastic cell wall, pushing up against it. It keeps the plant upright and prevents wilting.

**Page 33**
1. Light, wind, temperature, humidity.
2. Cooling the plant, providing water, providing minerals, support and photosynthesis.
3. Xylem vessels are thick hollow tubes made of dead cells. Phloem is a column of living cells.

**Page 36**
1. Nitrates, phosphates, potassium (compounds).
2. It will have poor growth and yellow leaves.
3. Microbes, warmth, oxygen, moisture.
4. **Any six from:** Canning; Cooling; Freezing; Drying; Adding salt; Adding sugar; Pickling.

**Page 39**
1. Fish farming, glasshouses, hydroponics, battery farming.
2. **Any two from:** Crops are lost to pests and diseases; Organic fertilisers take time to rot and don't supply a specific balance of minerals; Expensive; More space is needed.
3. Better control of mineral levels; Better control of disease.

**Answers to Exam Practice Questions**
1. a) Bacteria; Fungi; Saprophyte; Decomposer **[Any one for 1]**
   b) To add more oxygen **[1]** which would allow the detritivores to respire quicker **[1]** so the matter will decompose more quickly. **[1]** If he doesn't do this, the rate of decay would decrease as there would be less oxygen for the detritivores **[1]**.
   c) Warm; Damp; Oxygen **[All three for 1]**
2. a) Xylem transports water and soluble mineral salts **[1]** from the roots to the leaves. **[1]**
   b) **1–4 In any order:** Light; Air movement; Temperature; Humidity. **[All correct for 2]**
3. Has 6 legs; Has wings.
4. a) Quadrat
   b) Set an area; Place quadrats randomly within the area; Count the number of different plant species; Repeat several times. **[Any three for 3]**
   c) Transect
5. a) Nitrates / Nitrogen
   b) Potassium
   c) Behind library
6. a) 0
   b) Water moves from the solution into the potato by osmosis.
   c) Repeat the investigation and calculate a mean.
7. a) C **should be ticked**
   b) To allow sunlight through to the layer below.

# Chemistry

## Fundamental Chemical Concepts

**Quick Test Answers**
**Page 45**
1. Electrons
2. In the nucleus.
3. A charged atom or group of atoms that has lost or gained electrons.
4. The different types of atom in a compound; The number of each type of atom; Where the bonds are in the compound.

## C3 Chemical Economics

**Quick Test Answers**
**Page 49**
1. A measure of the amount of product made in a specific time.
2. g/s or g/min.
3. Increase temperature, increase concentration (for reactants that are in solution) or increase pressure (for reactants that are gases) or add a catalyst.
4. The reactant particles have more energy (kinetic) and move around faster, making them more likely to collide and collisions are higher energy making them more likely to form a product.

**Page 54**
1. $10 \div 44 \times 100 = 22.7\%$
2. Atom economy = $M_r$ of desired products $\div$ sum of $M_r$ of all products $\times$ 100
3. a) methane + oxygen → carbon dioxide + water
   b) Exothermic.

**Page 57**
1. **Any suitable answer, e.g.** Medicines; Pharmaceutical drugs.
2. Crushing, boiling, dissolving and chromatography.
3. Diamond, graphite and Buckminster fullerene.
4. $C_{60}$

**Answers to Exam Practice Questions**
1. a) i) $(2 \times 23) + 12 + (3 \times 16) = 106$ **[1 for calculation; 1 for correct answer]**
      ii) $(14 + [1 \times 4]) \times 2 + 32 + (4 \times 16) = 132$ **[2 for calculation; 1 for correct answer]**
   b) $9 \div 15 \times 100 = 60\%$ **[1 for calculation; 1 for correct answer]**
2. a) The materials for the new drug could be rare or may require expensive extraction from plants.
   b) You can make a product quickly on demand **[1]**; You can make a product on a small scale **[1]**; The equipment can be used to make a variety of products **[1]**.
3. a) They must collide **[1]** with sufficient energy **[1]**.
   b) There are more particles in the same volume, so they are more crowded **[1]**, and more particles collide more often **[1]**.
   c) The particles move faster **[1]**, causing them to collide more often and with more energy, resulting in successful collisions, and so an increase in rate of reaction. **[1]**
4. A powdered solid has a greater surface area in relation to its volume **[1]**. This increases the chance of collision **[1]** and speeds up the reaction. **[1]**
5. a) Time
   b) $40cm^3$
   c) **Accept any number between** 4.5 **and** 5 minutes.
6. a) Temperature; Concentration of solutions; Pressure of gases; Presence of a catalyst. **[Any two for 2]**
   b) Calculate the gradient at a given point of the line of best fit.
7. a) $4Fe + 3O_2 \rightarrow 2Fe_2O_3$ **[1 for correct reactants, 1 for correct products, 1 for correct balancing]**
   b) $(2 \times 56) + (3 \times 16) = 160$ **[1 for calculation, 1 for correct answer]**
   c) $4Fe + 3O_2 \rightarrow 2Fe_2O_3$ **[1]**
      $(4 \times 56) + 3 \times (16 \times 2) = 2 \times 160$ **[1 for correct calculation for reactions, 1 for correct calculation for products]**
      $320 = 320$ **[1]**

## C4 The Periodic Table

**Quick Test Answers**
**Page 62**
1. Protons and neutrons.
2. A substance made of only one type of atom.
3. **a)** F **b)** 19 **c)** 9 **d)** 10

**Page 67**
1. Each sodium atom loses one electron from its outer shell to become a $1^+$ ion.
2. The force of attraction between oppositely charged ions.
3. **a)** When molten or dissolved in water. **b)** MgO
4. A shared pair of electrons.

**Page 69**
1. All the elements have one electron in their outer shell.
2. Red

**Page 73**
1. All the elements have seven electrons in their outer shell.
2. Iron.
3. When a substance is broken down into two or more substances using heat.

**Page 75**
1. Run-off from fertilisers.
2. a) Barium chloride.
   b) sodium chloride + silver nitrate → silver chloride + sodium nitrate
3. a) Insoluble particles sink and can be removed.
   b) Chlorine.

**Answers to Exam Practice Questions**
1. a) A charged atom or group of atoms.
   b) Add 1 electron.
   c) High melting point; High boiling point; Conducts electricity in solution or when molten but not when solid.
2. a) Non-metals.
   b) There are no free-moving charged particles (electrons or ions) to carry the electricity.
   c) Group 4, period 3.
   d) They react with air **[1]** and water. **[1]**
   e) lithium + water → lithium hydroxide + hydrogen **[All correct for 2]**

# Answers

3.  **a)** Covalent bonding.
    **b)** 1 magnesium atom, 2 nitrogen atoms, 6 oxygen atoms.
    **c)** $2Na + 2H_2O \rightarrow 2NaOH + H_2$
4.  **a)** Breaking up a substance [1] using heat. [1]
    **b)** copper carbonate $\rightarrow$ copper oxide + carbon dioxide [All correct for 2]
    **c)** Iron(III)
5.  **a)** Chlorine.
    **b)** sodium iodide + chlorine $\rightarrow$ sodium chloride + iodine [All correct for 2]

**c)** $2NaI + Cl_2 \rightarrow 2NaCl + I_2$ [All correct for 2]
**d)** $Br_2 + 2e^- \rightarrow 2Br^-$ [All correct for 2]
6.  **This is a model answer, which demonstrates QWC and therefore would score the full 6 marks:** The halogens have similar properties because when they react they all lose one electron to become a halide, negative ion. The halogens become less reactive as you go down the group. As you go down the group, the atoms become larger, with the outer shell electrons further away from the attractive positive force of the nucleus. This makes it more difficult for the atom to gain an additional electron.

# Physics

## P3 Forces for Transport

**Quick Test Answers**
**Page 79**
1.  Distance and time     2.  Speed
**Page 81**
1.  Acceleration = Change in speed ÷ Time taken
2.  It is slowing down, deceleration at a rate of $5m/s^2$
**Page 87**
1.  ABS; Traction control; Cruise control; Paddle shifts.
2.  A deflector.
3.  It decreases.
**Page 89**
1.  Weight and air resistance.     2.  It stays the same.
**Page 91**
1.  It quadruples.     2.  10N/kg     3.  Joules (J)
**Answers to Exam Practice Questions**
1.  **a)** Change in speed; Time taken
    **b)** Straight line with a positive gradient — Constant speed
    Straight line with a negative gradient $\times$ Deceleration
    Horizontal straight line — Acceleration
    [All correct for 2]
2.  **a)** Graph line C
    **b)** At 45 mph, braking distance is 32m (**accept** 30–34m)
    **c)** Thinking distance is increased if the vehicle is travelling faster; If the driver is ill; If the driver is tired; If the driver is under the influence of alcohol or drugs.
3.  **a)** Mass and Speed.
    **b)** Kinetic energy = $0.5 \times 2000 \times 20^2$ = 400 000J [1 for calculation, 1 for correct answer]
4.  Air bags; Crumple zones; Seatbelts; Safety cages. [Any three for 3]
5.  A2; B4; C1; D3 [All correct for 3]
6.  Height = $\frac{\text{Potential energy}}{(\text{mass} \times g)}$ = $\frac{30}{(0.16 \times 10)}$ = 18.75m [1 for calculation, 1 for correct answer]
7.  **a)** Change in momentum = $m_1v_1 - m_2v_2$ = (1100 × 22.3)– (1100 × 13.4) = 24530 − 14740 = 9790kgm/s [1 for calculation, 1 for correct answer]
    **b)  i)** Change in momentum = $m_1v_1 - m_2v_2$ = (1100 × 13.4)– (1100 × 0) = 14740kgm/s
        [1 for calculation, 1 for correct answer]
    **ii)** Force = change in momentum ÷ time = 14740 ÷ 2.2 = 6700N [1 for calculation, 1 for correct answer]
8.  $h = v^2 \div 2g$; $v^2 = 2gh = 2 \times 10 \times 30 = 600$
    $v = \sqrt{600}$ = 24.5m/s. [2 for calculation, 1 for correct answer]

## P4 Radiation for Life

**Quick Test Answers**
**Page 96**
1.  Positive and negative.
2.  Re-start a heart which has stopped.
3.  Lose electrons.
**Page 99**
1.  $R = \frac{V}{I}$
2.  Live – brown; Neutral – blue; Earth – green and yellow.
3.  Melts and breaks.
4.  Fires (flex overheating); Injury to user; Damage to components.
**Page 101**
1.  The number of waves that pass a point in 1 second.
2.  **Any two from:** Scanning the body; Breaking down kidney stones; Measuring the speed of blood flow; Foetal scanning.
3.  It can be used to look at soft tissue and it does not damage living cells.
**Page 104**
1.  By the number of nuclear decays emitted per second.
2.  False
3.  A helium nucleus (made up of two protons and two neutrons).
4.  A proton and an electron.
**Page 109**
1.  Alpha, beta and gamma.
2.  Gamma
3.  Beta
**Answers to Exam Practice Questions**
1.  **a)** False. Electrons have a negative charge.
    **b)** Spray-painting; Smoke precipitators; Defibrillators [Any two for 2]
2.  **a)** Neutral — Green and yellow
    Earth $\times$ Brown
    Live — Blue     [All correct for 2]
    **b)** False. They still require a fuse to protect the appliance.
3.  **a)** $R = \frac{V}{I} = \frac{12}{0.3}$ = 40 ohms [1 for calculation, 1 for correct answer]
    **b)** $I = \frac{V}{R} = \frac{12}{80}$ = 0.15A [1 for calculation, 1 for correct answer]
4.  **This is a model answer, which demonstrates QWC and therefore would score the full 6 marks:** Nuclear fusion is the process by which heat energy is released when nuclei fuse together, for example in stars and fusion bombs. A large amount of heat energy is released. Nuclear fusion can only happen at extremely high temperatures. However, it is very difficult to manage such high temperatures, which means that nuclear fusion is not yet a possible energy resource on Earth.
5.  **a)** 8 days
    **b)** Yes, caesium-137 has a half-life of 30 years; so after only four months it is still extremely radioactive; and poses a severe health hazard.

**Acceleration** – the rate at which an object changes its velocity.

**Adaptation** – the gradual change of a particular organism over generations to become better suited to its environment.

**Aerobic respiration** – respiration using oxygen, which releases energy and produces carbon dioxide and water.

**Air resistance** – the frictional force that acts on a moving object.

**Allotropes** – different structural forms of the same element, e.g. diamond and graphite are both forms of carbon with different molecular structures.

**Anaerobic respiration** – releasing energy from glucose in living cells in the absence of oxygen to produce a small amount of energy very quickly.

**Artery** – large blood vessel with narrow lumen and thick elastic walls (carries blood away from the lungs).

**Asexual** – reproduction with no parent; offspring are clones.

**Atom** – the smallest part of an element that can enter into chemical reactions.

**Atom economy** – a measure of how many atoms from the reactants are in the desired product.

**Atomic number** – the number of protons in an atom; the number underneath the symbol in the periodic table.

**Attraction** – the drawing together of materials with different charges.

**Batch process** – a process where chemicals are added into a container, the reaction takes place, and the products are removed before a new reaction is started.

**Braking distance** – the distance a car travels during braking to a stop.

**Calorimeter** – a container used to hold liquids during a calorimetry experiment.

**Calorimetry** – an experiment used to measure the amount of energy released by a fuel or energy change in a reaction.

**Capillary** – a blood vessel that connects arteries to veins; where the exchange of materials takes place.

**Catalyst** – a substance that is used to speed up a chemical reaction without being chemically altered itself.

**Chlorophyll** – the green pigment found in most plants; responsible for photosynthesis.

**Chromosome** – a coil of DNA made up of genes, found in the nucleus of plants/animal cells.

**Circuit breaker** – electrical switch which protects a circuit from damage.

**Clone** – a genetically identical offspring of an organism.

**Collision** – when two or more particles hit each other.

**Compound** – a substance consisting of two or more elements chemically bonded.

**Compression** – area of high pressure in a medium caused by a wave, e.g. sound.

**Concentration** – a measure of the amount of substance dissolved in a solution.

**Conductor** – material that transfers thermal or electrical energy.

**Continuous process** – a process that doesn't stop; reactants are fed in at one end and products are removed at the other end at the same time.

**Covalent bond** – a bond between two atoms in which one or more pairs of electrons are shared.

**Current** – the rate of flow of an electrical charge; measured in amperes (A).

**Cytoplasm** – the jelly-like substance found in living cells where chemical reactions take place.

**Data** – information collected from an experiment/investigation.

**Decay** – rotting, breaking down.

**Decomposers** – organisms that break down dead plants or animals into simpler substances.

**Denature** – to irreversibly change the structure of a protein molecule.

**Detritivore** – an organism that feeds on dead organisms and the waste of living organisms.

**Detritus** – waste material formed from dead and decomposing plants and animals.

**Differentiation** – a process by which simple cells become specialised to perform a specific function.

**Diffusion** – the net movement of particles from an area of high concentration to an area of low concentration.

**Diploid** – a full chromosome set (i.e. 46), as found in most cells of the body.

**Distance–Time graph** – a graph showing distance travelled against time taken; the gradient of the line represents speed.

**DNA (deoxyribonucleic acid)** – the nucleic acid molecules that make up chromosomes in cells and carry genetic information.

**Double helix** – structure of DNA; twisted ladder structure.

**Earthed** – connecting the metal case of an electrical appliance to the earth wire of a plug.

**Ecosystem** – refers to a physical environment – the conditions there and the organisms that live there.

**Electromagnetic waves** – includes radio waves, visible light and gamma, all of which can travel through a vacuum at the speed of light.

**Electron** – a negatively charged particle that orbits the nucleus of an atom.

**Element** – a substance that consists of only one type of atom.

**Embryo** – an organism in the early stages of development in the uterus.

**Endothermic** – a reaction that takes in energy.

**Energy** – ability to do work; measured in joules.

**Enzyme** – a protein molecule and biological catalyst found in living organisms that helps chemical reactions to take place.

**Evaporation** – when particles gain enough energy to leave the liquid and become a gas.

**Exothermic** – a reaction that releases energy.

**Fertilisation** – the fusion of a male gamete with a female gamete.

**Fertiliser** – any substance used to make soil more fertile.

**Force** – a push or pull acting on an object; measured in newtons (N).

**Fossil fuel** – coal, oil and natural gas.

**Frequency** – the number of waves produced (or that pass a particular point) in one second.

# Glossary of Key Words

**Friction** – the resistive force between two surfaces as they move over each other.

**Fuse** – a thin piece of metal, which overheats and melts to break an electric circuit if it's overloaded.

**Gamete** – a specialised sex cell (egg and sperm).

**Gene** – a small section of DNA, in a chromosome, that determines a particular characteristic on its own or in combination with other genes.

**Genetic engineering/modification** – the alteration of the genetic make-up of an organism, e.g. by introducing new genes from another organism.

**Glucose** – a type of sugar; plants make this during photosynthesis.

**Gravitational potential energy (GPE)** – the energy an object has because of its mass and height above the Earth.

**Group** – a vertical column of elements in the periodic table.

**Haemoglobin** – the pigment that carries oxygen in the red blood cells.

**Half-life** – the time taken for half the atoms in radioactive material to decay.

**Halide** – a negative ion made from a Group 7 element that has gained one electron.

**Halogens** – elements in Group 7 of the periodic table.

**Haploid** – a cell that contains just one copy of each chromosome (i.e. 23 chromosomes).

**Hydroponics** – a method of growing plants in a solution instead of soil or compost.

**Hydroxide** – an OH⁻ ion.

**Hypothesis** – a scientific explanation that will be tested through experiments.

**Insoluble** – a substance that is unable to dissolve in a solvent.

**Insulator** – a substance that doesn't transfer thermal or electrical energy.

**Intensive farming** – farming which uses fertilisers and labour-saving technologies including pesticides and machinery.

**Ion** – a positively or negatively charged particle formed when an atom or group of atoms gains or loses one or more electron(s).

**Ionic bond** – the bond formed when electrons are transferred between a metal and a non-metal atom, creating charged ions that are then held together by forces of attraction.

**Ionising** – radiation that turns atoms into ions.

**Isotopes** – atoms of the same element which contain different numbers of neutrons.

**Joule (J)** – unit of energy.

**Kinetic energy (KE)** – the energy possessed by a body because of its movement.

**Lactic acid** – a waste product from anaerobic respiration in animals.

**Longitudinal wave** – a wave where the particles vibrate in the direction of energy transfer.

**Mass** – the quantity of matter in an object.

**Mass number** – the total number of protons and neutrons in an atom.

**Meiosis** – cell division in reproductive tissue, which produces gametes with a half-chromosome set.

**Meristem** – an area where unspecialised cells divide, producing plant growth, e.g. roots, shoots.

**Microorganism** – an organism that can only be seen with a microscope, e.g. bacteria.

**Meiosis** – cell division in reproductive tissue, which produces gametes with a half-chromosone set.

**Mitochondria** – the structures in the cytoplasm of a cell where energy is produced through respiration reactions.

**Mitosis** – the type of cell division that forms two daughter cells, each with the same number of chromosomes as the parent cell.

**Model** – a representation of a system or idea, used to describe or explain the system or idea.

**Momentum** – a measure of the state of motion of an object as a product of its mass and velocity.

**Mutation** – a spontaneous change in the genetic material of a cell.

**Nanochemistry** – the study of materials that have a very small size, in the order of 1–100nm; one nanometre is one billionth of a metre and can be written as 1nm or 1m × 10⁻⁹.

**Neutron** – a sub-atomic particle found in the nucleus of atoms; it has no charge.

**Nuclear fission** – the splitting of atomic nuclei.

**Nuclear fusion** – the release of heat energy when two nuclei join together.

**Nucleus** – the core of an atom, made up of protons and neutrons (except hydrogen, which contains a single proton).

**Octet** – eight electrons in the outer shell.

**Organic farming** – involves farming without the use of chemicals, artificial fertilisers, pesticides or herbicides.

**Osmosis** – the net movement of water particles from a dilute solution to a more concentrated solution across a partially permeable membrane.

**Period** – a horizontal row of elements in the periodic table.

**Pest** – an organism that causes damage or harm.

**Pesticide** – a chemical that kills pests.

**Photosynthesis** – the chemical process that takes place in green plants where water combines with carbon dioxide to produce glucose using light energy.

**Pollutant** – a chemical that can harm the environment and organisms.

**Pollution** – the contamination of an environment by chemicals, waste or heat.

**Pooter** – apparatus used to collect insects.

**Population** – a group of organisms of the same species living in a defined area.

**Power** – the rate of doing work; measured in watts (W).

**Precipitate** – an insoluble solid formed during a reaction involving ionic solutions.

**Precipitation** – the formation of an insoluble solid (a precipitate) when two solutions containing ions are mixed together.

**Predator** – an animal that hunts, kills and eats its prey.

**Pressure** – the amount of gas particles in a volume. It is like concentration for a gas.

**Product** – a substance made in a chemical reaction.

**Proteins** – large organic compounds made of amino acids; needed in the diet for growth and repair.

**Proton** – a positively charged sub-atomic particle found in the nucleus of an atom.

**Quadrat** – a square of known size used in ecology to sample an area randomly.

**Radiation** – electromagnetic waves/particles emitted by a radioactive substance.

**Radioactive** – substance that emits radiation from its atomic nuclei.

**Radioisotope** – a radioactive isotope of an element.

**Rarefaction** – area of low pressure in a medium caused by a wave, e.g. sound.

**Reactant** – a starting material in a reaction.

**Recovery rate** – the time it takes for your heart rate to return to normal after exercise.

**Relative atomic mass ($A_r$)** – the mass of an atom compared to a twelfth of the mass of a carbon-12 atom.

**Relative formula mass ($M_r$)** – the sum of the atomic masses of all the atoms in a compound.

**Relative speed** – the speed of an object, relative to another object that is being treated to be at rest.

**Repulsion** – the pushing away of materials that have the same charge.

**Resistance** – how hard it is to get a current through a component at a particular potential difference; measured in ohms ($\Omega$).

**Respiration** – a process that takes place in cells, which releases energy from glucose.

**Salt** – the product of a chemical reaction between a base and an acid.

**Selective breeding** – the process by which animals are selected and mated to produce offspring with desirable characteristics.

**Soluble** – when a substance dissolves.

**Speed** – the rate at which an object moves.

**Speed–Time graph** – a graph showing speed against time; the gradient of the line represents acceleration.

**Stable** – does not react.

**Static electricity** – build up of charge in a substance.

**Stem cells** – cells from human embryos or adult bone marrow that have yet to differentiate.

**Stomata** – the tiny openings on a plant leaf used for gas exchange.

**Sweepnet** – a large net used to catch insects so they can be counted or studied.

**Terminal speed** – a steady falling speed, when the weight of an object is equal and opposite to the air resistance on it.

**Thinking distance** – the distance that a car travels whilst the driver reacts and starts to brake.

**Tracer** – a radioactive substance that can be followed and detected.

**Transect** – a sampling method.

**Transfer** – moving energy from one place to another.

**Transformer** – an electrical device that changes the voltage of alternating currents.

**Translocation** – the transportation of food through phloem in plants.

**Transpiration** – the loss of water (by diffusion and evaporation) from plants, especially from their leaves.

**Ultrasound** – sound waves with a frequency above 20 000Hz.

**Variable** – something that changes during the course of an experiment/investigation.

**Vein** – a type of blood vessel that transports blood towards the heart.

**Voltage (potential difference)** – the difference in potential between two points in an electrical circuit; the energy transferred in a circuit by each Coulomb of charge; measured in volts (V).

**Wavelength** – the distance between corresponding points on two adjacent disturbances.

**Weight** – the gravitational force that pulls an object towards the centre of the Earth.

**Yield** – the amount of product obtained, e.g. from a crop or a chemical reaction.

---

(HT) **Active transport** – the movement of substances against a concentration gradient; requires energy.

**Distillation** – a process used to separate liquids by evaporation followed by condensation to produce a pure liquid.

**Electron configuration** – the arrangement of electrons in the shell of an atom or ion.

**Flaccid** – a plant cell that isn't rigid; it is floppy due to lack of water.

**Isotope** – one or more atoms with the same atomic number but different mass numbers.

**Limiting factor** – a factor that limits the rate of reaction.

**Oxyhaemoglobin** – haemoglobin combined with oxygen.

**Plasmolysis** – the contraction of the inside of plant cells due to the loss of water.

**Ribosomes** – tiny organelles in the cell that carry out protein synthesis.

**Saprophytes** – bacteria and fungi that feed on dead organic material.

**Turgid** – a rigid plant cell.

**Zonation** – distribution of organisms in an area; sampling method.

# Periodic Table

118

**Key**

relative atomic mass
**atomic symbol**
name
atomic (proton) number

| 1 | 1 | | | | | | | | | | | | | | | | |
|---|---|---|---|---|---|---|---|---|---|---|---|---|---|---|---|---|---|
| **H** | | | | | | | | | | | | | | | | | |
| hydrogen | | | | | | | | | | | | | | | | | |
| 1 | | | | | | | | | | | | | | | | | |

| 1 | 2 | | | | | | | | | | | 3 | 4 | 5 | 6 | 7 | 0 |
|---|---|---|---|---|---|---|---|---|---|---|---|---|---|---|---|---|---|
| | | | | | | | | | | | | | | | | | 4 **He** helium 2 |
| 7 **Li** lithium 3 | 9 **Be** beryllium 4 | | | | | | | | | | | 11 **B** boron 5 | 12 **C** carbon 6 | 14 **N** nitrogen 7 | 16 **O** oxygen 8 | 19 **F** fluorine 9 | 20 **Ne** neon 10 |
| 23 **Na** sodium 11 | 24 **Mg** magnesium 12 | | | | | | | | | | | 27 **Al** aluminium 13 | 28 **Si** silicon 14 | 31 **P** phosphorus 15 | 32 **S** sulfur 16 | 35.5 **Cl** chlorine 17 | 40 **Ar** argon 18 |
| 39 **K** potassium 19 | 40 **Ca** calcium 20 | 45 **Sc** scandium 21 | 48 **Ti** titanium 22 | 51 **V** vanadium 23 | 52 **Cr** chromium 24 | 55 **Mn** manganese 25 | 56 **Fe** iron 26 | 59 **Co** cobalt 27 | 59 **Ni** nickel 28 | 63.5 **Cu** copper 29 | 65 **Zn** zinc 30 | 70 **Ga** gallium 31 | 73 **Ge** germanium 32 | 75 **As** arsenic 33 | 79 **Se** selenium 34 | 80 **Br** bromine 35 | 84 **Kr** krypton 36 |
| 85 **Rb** rubidium 37 | 88 **Sr** strontium 38 | 89 **Y** yttrium 39 | 91 **Zr** zirconium 40 | 93 **Nb** niobium 41 | 96 **Mo** molybdenum 42 | [98] **Tc** technetium 43 | 101 **Ru** ruthenium 44 | 103 **Rh** rhodium 45 | 106 **Pd** palladium 46 | 108 **Ag** silver 47 | 112 **Cd** cadmium 48 | 115 **In** indium 49 | 119 **Sn** tin 50 | 122 **Sb** antimony 51 | 128 **Te** tellurium 52 | 127 **I** iodine 53 | 131 **Xe** xenon 54 |
| 133 **Cs** caesium 55 | 137 **Ba** barium 56 | 139 **La*** lanthanum 57 | 178 **Hf** hafnium 72 | 181 **Ta** tantalum 73 | 184 **W** tungsten 74 | 186 **Re** rhenium 75 | 190 **Os** osmium 76 | 192 **Ir** iridium 77 | 195 **Pt** platinum 78 | 197 **Au** gold 79 | 201 **Hg** mercury 80 | 204 **Tl** thallium 81 | 207 **Pb** lead 82 | 209 **Bi** bismuth 83 | [209] **Po** polonium 84 | [210] **At** astatine 85 | [222] **Rn** radon 86 |
| [223] **Fr** francium 87 | [226] **Ra** radium 88 | [227] **Ac*** actinium 89 | [261] **Rf** rutherfordium 104 | [262] **Db** dubnium 105 | [266] **Sg** seaborgium 106 | [264] **Bh** bohrium 107 | [277] **Hs** hassium 108 | [268] **Mt** meitnerium 109 | [271] **Ds** darmstadtium 110 | [272] **Rg** roentgenium 111 | | | | | | | |

Elements with atomic numbers 112–116 have been reported but not fully authenticated

*The lanthanoids (atomic numbers 58–71) and the actinoids (atomic numbers 90–103) have been omitted.